Vocabulary and Spelling Book

McDougal Littell

GRADE SEVEN

McDougal Littell
A HOUGHTON MIFFLIN COMPANY
Evanston, Illinois   Boston   Dallas

ISBN-13: 978-0-618-13668-1   ISBN-10: 0-618-13668-1

16 17 18 0956 13 12 11 10
4500232927

Contents

Academic Vocabulary Lessons (continued)

Spelling Lessons

Vocabulary

Tools for Vocabulary Study

The *Vocabulary and Spelling Book* contains lessons designed to help you understand and remember important vocabulary skills and strategies. You will often need to use basic reference sources to master these new techniques and to complete the exercises within the book. Use the information below to help you in your work.

Using References

Dictionaries

A **dictionary** can tell you more than just what a word means. It can also provide the pronunciation of a word, its etymology (origin), and connotations that might concern the reader. Look at the following dictionary entries to see some of the many details a dictionary can offer.

Guide Words—First and Last Words on the Page

Entry Word Divided into Syllables

Different **Pronunciations** for Different Definitions

Definitions

Synonyms

Label Identifying Special Usage

Parts of Speech Being Defined

Etymology

Other Forms of Entry Word

offense   **ogle**

of•fense (ə fĕns′) *n.* **1.** The act of offending. **2.** A violation of a moral or social code. **3.** A crime. **4.** (ŏf′ĕns′). [<Lat. *offendere,* offend.]

of•fen•sive (ə fĕn′siv) *adj.* **1.** Disagreeable to the senses. **2.** Causing anger, resentment, or affront. **3.** Making an attack. **4.** (ŏf′ĕns)—*Sports.* Relating to the offense. –**of•fen•sive•ly** *adv.* –**of•fen•sive•ness** *n.*
Syns: disgusting, loathsome, nasty, repellent, repulsive, revolting *adj.*

of•fer (ô′fər, ŏf′ər) *v.* **1.** To present for acceptance or rejection. **2.** To present for sale. **3.** To present as payment; bid. **4.** To present as an act of worship. **5.** To put up; mount. **6.** To produce or introduce on the stage. [<Lat. *offerre* : *ob-,* to + *ferre,* bring.] –**of•fer** *n.* –**of•fer•er, of•fer•or** *n.*

of•fi•ci•ate (ə-fĭsh′ē-āt′) *v.* –**at•ed,** –**at•ing. 1.** To perform the functions of an office or position of authority, esp. at a religious service. **2.** *Sports.* to serve as a referee or umpire. –**of•fi•ci•a•tor** *n.*

—adapted from *The American Heritage Student Dictionary*

Dictionaries frequently list several definitions for the same word. How do you know which definition is the right one for your purposes?

Here's How

Choosing the Right Definition

1. Read through all the definitions in the dictionary entry.

2. Decide which definition best fits the meaning of the sentence in which you found the word. For example, "an offensive smell" probably matches the first definition given; "an offensive play in football" probably matches the fourth definition.

Thesauruses

A **thesaurus** is a dictionary of **synonyms.** Some thesauruses also include definitions, sample sentences, and **antonyms**—words that have opposite meanings to that of the entry word.

When you need to find a replacement for a word look up the word in the thesaurus. Entries are often listed in alphabetical order.

Part of Speech

offensive, *adj*

Definition

Utterly unpleasant or distasteful to the senses or sensibilities. **syn:** *atrocious, disgusting, evil, foul, hideous, horrible, horrid, revolting, sickening, ungrateful, unwholesome, vile* **ant:** *inoffensive, unoffensive*

Synonyms

Antonyms

Context Clues

Lesson 1

One way to figure out the meaning of a word that you do not know is by looking it up in a dictionary. Another way is to look for clues in the words that surround it—that is, its **context**. Consider the word *frail*. Its dictionary definition is "delicate; weak and fragile." You can also figure out the word's general meaning by using context clues. Consider the following sentence:

Weak and tired after a long day, the little girl was in a **frail** state.

The meaning of the word *frail* is given in the context clue, "weak and tired."

A. Context Clues in Action

In each sentence below, underline the context clues that help you understand the general meaning of the italicized word. Write what you think the word means on the first line. Then check your answer using a dictionary.

1. For your persuasive argument to be *effective*, you need to convince your audience with relevant facts, statistics, and examples.

   your definition: _____

   dictionary definition: _____

2. Stop teasing me! Just because you are a better tennis player doesn't mean you should *belittle* my abilities.

   your definition: _____

   dictionary definition: _____

3. Climbing the rocky hill made me *falter*, and I almost fell.

   your definition: _____

   dictionary definition: _____

4. The way he lurked in the shadows increased our *suspicion* of the stranger.

   your definition: _____

   dictionary definition: _____

5. When her two best friends argue, Rachel remains *neutral*, refusing to take sides.

   your definition: _____

   dictionary definition: _____

6. The sweater was of *inferior* quality—it was torn and had a missing button.

   your definition: _____

   dictionary definition: _____

7. They decided to go out in the boat after listening to a *favorable* weather forecast.

   your definition: _____

   dictionary definition: _____

8. It's hard to resist the *temptation* of a freshly baked apple pie on the kitchen counter.

   your definition: _____

   dictionary definition: _____

9. I look neat, tidy, and *presentable*.

   your definition: _____

   dictionary definition: _____

10. Your behavior has earned my *mistrust*; I don't have any confidence in you.

    your definition: _____

    dictionary definition: _____

Context Clues

More Practice

effective	falter	neutral	presentable	temptation
belittle	suspicion	inferior	favorable	mistrust

B. Vocabulary Words in Action

In each sentence, use a word from the vocabulary list above. Make sure the word
you choose fits the overall meaning of the sentence. Use a dictionary if needed.

1. Jack made a _____ impression on the other members and was quickly voted into the club.

2. She gave in easily to _____, which is why we weren't sure we could trust her.

3. Tara was careful not to stumble or _____ during her gymnastics routine.

4. People who think of others as _____, or beneath them, often find ways to tease or _____ them.

5. My _____ about the cookie thief was confirmed when I saw my little brother wiping the crumbs from his mouth. I always _____, or doubt, him around his favorite foods!

6. Most of my friends have strong feelings on the issue, but I am _____.

7. Her years in student government helped make her a capable and _____ public speaker.

8. Combing my hair and washing my face made me look _____—appropriate to be seen by others.

C. Vocabulary Challenge

Read the following sentences and underline each of the context clues. Then add
the correct vocabulary word to each sentence.

contagious	ambitious	obligation	flaw	secretive

1. His goals were _____, and he knew that it would take hard work and determination to reach them.

2. I promised to take care of the dog—he is my _____.

3. The nurse said Amber was _____ and sent her home from school to keep the other students from getting sick.

4. Being impatient is my worst _____; it is quite a shortcoming.

5. Because Joy sat quietly in the back of the class, the other students thought she was being _____.

Definition and Restatement Clues

Lesson 2

Teaching

Sometimes you can find the meaning of an unfamiliar word in the surrounding text. One type of context clue is **definition**, in which a writer uses an unfamiliar word and then explains what it means, usually within the next sentence or two. Another type of context clue is **restatement**, in which a writer expresses the same idea using different language. Consider the following example:

> John was *enfeebled* by his sickness. Weakened and weary, he was unable to play baseball on Saturday.

The writer uses the phrase *weakened and weary* to restate the meaning of *enfeebled*.

A. Definition and Restatement Clues in Action

In the sentences below, underline the definition or restatement context clue for the word in *italic type*. Then, on a separate sheet of paper, write a new sentence using that word. Use a dictionary if needed.

1. Olympic gymnasts are very *limber*, or flexible, allowing them to perform their skillful movements.

2. The volcano could *erupt* at any moment; when it does explode, the result will be deadly.

3. They decided to *unite* against the class bully, hoping that their joint effort would put him in his place.

4. Jenny's long *exposure* to the tropical sun was obvious. Unprotected, her face and neck had reddened and started to peel.

5. Based on his *recollection*, they had met last month at the dog park. However, his memory was not as good as it used to be.

6. It is important to *gauge* how long you think this trip will take. By making an estimated measurement, you can plan your time accordingly.

7. Karen did not wish to *violate* her parents rules, even if her older brother broke them constantly.

8. If you don't water the flowers, they will *wilt* or lose their strength and freshness.

9. Dan is a *compassionate* person. His words and actions show how kind-hearted he is.

10. I wish you wouldn't *rummage* through my suitcase. After all, I don't search through your things.

Definition and Restatement Clues

Lesson 2

More Practice

| limber | unite | recollection | violate | rummage |
| erupt | exposure | gauge | wilt | compassionate |

B. Vocabulary Words in Action

For each sentence, choose the correct word from the vocabulary list above. Remember to read each sentence using the vocabulary word you choose to make sure it fits the overall meaning. Use a dictionary if needed.

1. If you _____, or disobey, the agreement, you will be punished for it. Don't expect us

   to be gentle and _____ with you!

2. Stretching before you exercise will help make your joints more _____, or able to be stretched.

3. Dad will _____ in anger when he finds out what we did. He will be like a volcano!

4. According to my _____, I haven't been sick in ages. My memory isn't perfect, though.

5. For a science experiment, we will _____, or measure, this month's rainfall.

6. We must _____ on this issue and work together.

7. The spy decided to _____ and search through files. She was looking for secrets

   worthy of _____—bringing into the open.

8. After working for hours under this hot sun, I am about to _____—and faint!

B. Vocabulary Challenge

Use a dictionary to look up definitions for the italicized words. Then rewrite each sentence to include context clues that would help a reader understand what the vocabulary word means.

1. Water damage caused our floorboards to *warp*.

   _____

2. She liked to use *vivid* colors in her paintings.

   _____

3. If you don't want the sweater, you can bring it back to the store for a full *refund*.

   _____

4. In case of a flood, make sure you have enough *provisions* to last a week.

   _____

5. It was a common *trait* of hers to laugh uncontrollably for no reason.

   _____

Lesson 3 # Definition, Restatement, and Example Clues *Teaching*

One way to figure out the meaning of an unfamiliar word is to look for surrounding context clues. A writer may **define** (give the meaning of) the word elsewhere in a sentence. The writer may **restate** the word, describing the same idea in language you are more likely to understand. For example:

Lily possessed an *indomitable* energy, one that could not be conquered.

Using the definition context clues, you can infer that *indomitable* means "unconquerable."

The writer may also give one or more **examples** to help you understand the difficult words.

Amphibians such as frogs and salamanders can live in the water and on land.

This sentence gives two examples of amphibians—frogs and salamanders—and a definition of the term ("can live in the water or on land").

A. Definition, Restatement, and Example Clues in Action

For each item, circle the context clue that shows the meaning of the word in *italic type.* Then write a synonym for the meaning you infer on the lines provided. Use a dictionary if needed.

1. Jennifer wanted to travel *abroad* to a foreign land. _____

2. Stop *brooding*! Moping and worrying like that won't help. _____

3. Lara brought food and other *provisions* on her camping trip. _____

4. If you don't make *haste* you'll never get there in time. _____

5. This material is very *flimsy*; it will tear. _____

6. You will succeed if you are a *shrewd,* clever person. _____

7. Before I *reveal* what's behind my back, can you guess what it is? _____

8. The *typhoon's* winds were violent and destructive. _____

9. *Rotate* your bicycle wheels by turning them to make them less squeaky. _____

10. We are sending shirts and other *apparel* to children in need. _____

Definition, Restatement, and Example Clues

Lesson 3

| abroad | apparel | flimsy | reveal | rotate |
| brooding | haste | shrewd | typhoon | provisions |

B. Vocabulary Words in Action

For each item, use a word from the vocabulary list above. Read each sentence with your word choice to make sure it fits the overall meaning. Use a dictionary if needed.

1. Are you sure we packed enough _____, or supplies for the trip?

2. Daria kept puzzling and _____ over her disastrous science project.

3. Once Phil gets to know you, he will _____, or display a fun and lively side to himself.

4. The _____ politician knew just what he needed to do to get the votes.

5. The wood used for this boat is very _____; are you sure it will float?

6. I lived _____ in Spain for several years before coming here.

7. Small children often like to _____ in swivel chairs until they become dizzy.

8. Because of inaccurate weather reporting, the _____ arrived in such

   _____ that we were unprepared for it.

9. What kind of _____ are you wearing tonight—casual clothes or something dressy?

C. Vocabulary Challenge

Use a dictionary to look up each word listed below. Then write one sentence using each word. In the sentence, provide a restatement clue, an example, or a definition of the listed word.

1. fundamental _____

   _____

2. hardy _____

   _____

3. devise _____

   _____

4. crevice _____

   _____

5. agile _____

   _____

Name _____ Date _____

Comparison and Contrast Clues

Teaching

Comparison clues are words and phrases that have the same or similar meaning as an unfamiliar word. Words and phrases such as *like, as,* and *in the same way* often signal comparisons. **Contrast clues** are words and phrases that mean the opposite of an unfamiliar word. Words and phrases such as *although, but, yet, however, except* and *on the other hand* signal contrasts. In the sentence below, the word "as" signals the comparison between the clue, "ready to bite me," and the meaning of *menacing*—threatening.

The large dog seemed *menacing*, as if it were ready to bite me.

A. Comparison and Contrast Clues in Action

For each sentence, circle the word or phrase that signals a comparison or contrast clue. Circle *comparison* or *contrast*, depending on the type of clue. Then write the meaning of the underlined word. Use a dictionary if needed.

1. Sid thought the music would end gradually, but it stopped *abruptly* instead.

   comparison/contrast
   meaning: _____

2. When he wouldn't get his way, he would *sulk* like a child whose toys were taken away.

   comparison/contrast
   meaning: _____

3. Angela had hoped that the dress would fit, but after trying it on she realized she would have to make an *alteration*.

   comparison/contrast
   meaning: _____

4. The little girl was always *radiant*, as if the sun glowed on her face wherever she went.

   comparison/contrast
   meaning: _____

5. The students were *reluctant* to take the quiz—except Mary who had studied for it.

   comparison/contrast
   meaning: _____

6. Sarah wanted a *prominent* place in the class picture; however, I preferred to be in the background.

   comparison/contrast
   meaning: _____

7. Although others found him to be *disagreeable*, I thought he was quite pleasant.

   comparison/contrast
   meaning: _____

8. Don's efforts on the soccer field were *valiant* in the same way a soldier shows courage in battle.

   comparison/contrast
   meaning: _____

9. The teacher said my report was *satisfactory*, but I wish it could have been better.

   comparison/contrast
   meaning: _____

10. Although the dance routine seemed *intricate*, I thought it was quite simple.

    comparison/contrast
    meaning: _____

Name _____ Date _____

Comparison and Contrast Clues

More Practice

abruptly	*alteration*	*reluctant*	*disagreeable*	*satisfactory*
sulk	*radiant*	*prominent*	*valiant*	*intricate*

B. Vocabulary Words in Action

For each item, choose a word from the vocabulary list above and write it in the blank. Remember to read each sentence using the vocabulary word you choose to make sure it fits the overall meaning. Use a dictionary if needed.

1. Daryl's plan to win the game was as _____ as a 1,000-piece puzzle.

2. After a bad night's sleep, Jason was as _____ as an attack dog.

3. By her glowing, _____ smile, I knew she was pleased to be given a _____ role in the school play. She wouldn't be happy with a small part!

4. Instead of slowing gradually, the car braked _____ when a squirrel ran in front of it.

5. Our solution isn't perfect, but at least it is _____.

6. The experiment almost worked; I had to make just one small _____.

7. Rather than _____, try to make the most out of a difficult situation.

8. Although _____ at first, he overcame his fear and proved to be a _____ hero.

C. Vocabulary Challenge

Read the following sentences and try to pick out the context clues. Then circle the meaning of the italicized word. Finally, compare your definitions with those in the dictionary and see how you did.

1. She was *hostile* toward the stranger in the same way that an animal reacts when threatened.

   polite/unfriendly/playful

2. Although the fire was damaging, he was able to *salvage* some belongings.

   save/discard/return

3. Despite the fact that she was having a *routine* operation, Joan was still worried.

   rare/difficult/standard

4. Much like his parents, Charles respected the idea of family *tradition*.

   custom/resistance/anxiety

5. I proudly stood by my *conviction*, even though it went against the majority.

   shyness/belief/uncertainty

General Context Clues

Teaching

You already know that you can sometimes understand the meaning of a word by examining the context in which the word is used. Context clues can appear in the surrounding words, sentences, even paragraphs.

Consider the following passage from "A Crown of Wild Olive":

> He woke to the first *dappled* fingers of sunlight shafting in through the doorway of his cell. They wavered and danced a little, as though broken by the shadows of tree branches.

From the description of the light, you might infer that the word *dappled* means "having varying spots or patches of color."

A. General Context Clues in Action

Read the following sentences. Then use context clues to determine the meaning of each italicized word. Then write the meaning that you infer. Use a dictionary to confirm the meaning.

1. Samantha was the only one in her class to receive an award of *distinction.* At the awards ceremony, the principal mentioned Samantha's academic achievements and her performance on the soccer team and in the chorus.

   _____

2. Harry had an expression of extreme *anguish* on his face. "Something horrible has happened!" he gasped.

   _____

3. People who *compete* in sports tournaments enjoy testing their skills against other teams and athletes.

   _____

4. Shane just can't make up his mind. He often *wavers* between choices for hours without ever making a decision.

   _____

5. Carrie was very *impulsive,* often doing things without thinking.

   _____

Lesson 5 # General Context Clues

More Practice

distinction   *anguish*   *compete*   *waver*

B. Vocabulary Words in Action

For each blank, choose a word from the vocabulary list above. Read the paragraph to make sure the words you have filled in fit the overall meaning. Use a dictionary for extra help.

I wanted to _____ in the statewide spelling bee. Hundreds

of other students were taking part, and I had hopes of gaining

_____ for myself. After all, the winner gets a scholarship, a

plaque, and his or her name in the newspaper. I won three rounds, but my

joy turned to _____ when I was asked to spell

"perspicacious." (That means "clear-thinking.") I started to

_____ between one answer and another, not sure which to

give. I lost the spelling bee, but there's always next year!

C. Vocabulary Challenge

Choose the correct vocabulary word for each item and write it in the blank. Use a dictionary if needed.

efficient   *falsehood*   *victorious*   *solitary*

1. Always out with his friends, Daryl rarely has a _____ moment to himself.

2. This was yet another _____ in a long string of lies and tall tales.

3. Our team finally emerged _____ after two overtimes on the field.

4. When you have many chores to do, daydreaming is not an _____ use of your time.

Lesson 6

Prefixes and Base Words

Breaking a word down into its different parts is one way to understand the word's meaning. A **base word** is a complete word that can stand alone. It can also be combined with a word part, such as a **prefix,** to form a new word. A **prefix** attaches to the beginning of a base word, altering or adding meaning to it. For example, consider the word *impolite*.

(The prefix *im-* means "not")   (The base word *polite* means "courteous.")

impolite = im- + polite

(When the word parts are combined, *impolite* means "not courteous.")

The chart below lists eight common prefixes that mean "not" or "wrong":

Prefix	Meaning	Example
dis-	not, lack of	disagree
il-	not	illegal
im-	not	impolite
in-	not	incorrect
ir-	not	irreplaceable
mis-	wrong, wrongly	misbehave
non-	not	nonstop
un-	not, opposite	unfasten

A. Identifying Prefixes and Base Words

For each example in Column A, draw a line between the prefix and the base word. Then match each example in Column A with its correct meaning in Column B. Write the letter of the correct meaning in the space provided. Use a dictionary if necessary.

Column A

EXAMPLE   mis/judge __L__

1. misguide _____
2. illogical _____
3. unfamiliar _____
4. inactive _____
5. dishonest _____
6. irregular _____
7. immature _____
8. unhappy _____
9. mishandle _____
10. nonviolent _____

Column B

L. to conclude wrongly

A. not truthful

B. to manage wrongly

C. not sensible

D. not moving

E. to lead wrongly

F. not seen or known

G. not forceful

H. not pleased

I. not typical or even

J. not fully developed

Lesson 6

Prefixes and Base Words

B. Prefixes and Base Words in Action

Prefixes: *dis-, il-, im-, in-, ir-, mis-,* and *un-*.

Underline ten examples in the passage that begin with the prefixes listed above. Write the prefix and base word of each example. Then define each example using what you know about prefixes and context clues. Use a dictionary to check your answers.

I hope you don't think I'm impossible, but this dish is unfit to serve at the party. Did you forget to use a nonstick pan? Was the handwriting on the recipe card illegible? Fortunately, I think that we have enough time to correct this misstep. We certainly don't want to displease our guests by having an incomplete meal, or by serving an inedible dish. To do so would be quite irresponsible. Let's try to fix this unpleasant situation in a hurry!

1. prefix: _____ base word: _____ meaning: _____

2. prefix: _____ base word: _____ meaning: _____

3. prefix: _____ base word: _____ meaning: _____

4. prefix: _____ base word: _____ meaning: _____

5. prefix: _____ base word: _____ meaning: _____

6. prefix: _____ base word: _____ meaning: _____

7. prefix: _____ base word: _____ meaning: _____

8. prefix: _____ base word: _____ meaning: _____

9. prefix: _____ base word: _____ meaning: _____

10. prefix: _____ base word: _____ meaning: _____

C. Vocabulary Challenge

For each prefix below, provide three different base words. Then write a sentence using one of the new words. Use a dictionary to check your answers.

EXAMPLE ir- *resistible, replaceable, removable*
The children found the desserts irresistible and ate them first.

1. *im-* _____, _____, _____

_____

2. *mis-* _____, _____, _____

_____

3. *un-* _____, _____, _____

_____

Lesson 7 — Prefixes and Base Words

Teaching

You can use your knowledge of different word parts to figure out the meaning of many unfamiliar words. A **base word** is a complete word that can stand alone. A **prefix** is a word part that appears at the beginning of a base word to form a new word. For example, consider the word *prehistoric*.

(The prefix *pre-* means "before.")   (The base word *historic* means "based on events in history.")

pre + historic = prehistoric

(When the word parts are combined, *prehistoric* means "before recorded history.")

The chart below lists eight common prefixes.

Prefix	Meaning	Example
pre-	before	prepay
post-	after, later	postdate
inter-	among, between	interconnect
intra-	within	intramuscular
re-	back, again	reappear
sub-	under	subhuman
super-	above, beyond	superpower
trans-	across	transplant

A. Identifying Prefixes and Base Words

Add a prefix to each base word to create a word with the meaning shown. Then write a paragraph using each new word on a separate sheet of paper. Be creative.

EXAMPLE *super*human; beyond normal human ability

She used superhuman powers to lift the car off the boy's leg.

1. _____state; within the boundaries of a state

2. _____marine; a vehicle that operates under water

3. _____script; a note at the end of a letter after the writer's signature

4. _____school; education that comes before kindergarten

5. _____construct; to build again

6. _____continental; crossing a continent

7. _____liner; a passenger ship or train that is above others in quality and accomodation

8. _____planetary; occurring between planets

9. _____judge; to form an opinion beforehand

10. _____way; an underground tunnel or passage

Lesson 7 — Prefixes and Base Words

More Practice

B. Prefixes and Base Words in Action

Prefixes: *pre-, post-, inter-, intra-, re-, sub-, super-, trans-*

Underline ten examples in the passage that begin with the prefixes listed above. Write the prefix and base word of each example. Then define each example using what you know about prefixes and base words. Use a dictionary to check your answers.

In our postindustrial age, the Internet is a wonderful tool. The information superhighway provides millions of facts to users. Be aware, though, that some sites are substandard, offering inaccurate information. The Net also allows users to send e-mail messages both internationally and within a small group on the intranet. However, when sending a transatlantic (or overseas) message or creating a Web site, you should take sensible precautions. Never give your last name or reproduce your photo. Also, it may be a good idea to have an adult preview your site before you go public.

1. prefix: _____ base word: _____ meaning: _____

2. prefix: _____ base word: _____ meaning: _____

3. prefix: _____ base word: _____ meaning: _____

4. prefix: _____ base word: _____ meaning: _____

5. prefix: _____ base word: _____ meaning: _____

6. prefix: _____ base word: _____ meaning: _____

7. prefix: _____ base word: _____ meaning: _____

8. prefix: _____ base word: _____ meaning: _____

9. prefix: _____ base word: _____ meaning: _____

10. prefix: _____ base word: _____ meaning: _____

C. Vocabulary Challenge

For each prefix below, provide three different base words. Then write a sentence using one of the new words. Use a dictionary if necessary.

EXAMPLE sub- *zero, title, culture*
Most people would not be able to survive the Arctic's subzero temperatures.

1. *pre-* _____, _____, _____

_____

2. *inter-* _____, _____, _____

_____

Prefixes and Base Words

Lesson 8

One way to understand a word's meaning is to break it down into its different word parts. A **base word** is a complete word that can stand alone. A **prefix** is a word part that appears at the beginning of a base word to form a new word.

For example, consider the word *micromanage*.

(The prefix *micro-* means "small")   (The base word *manage* means "to handle or control.")

micromanage = micro- + manage.

(When the word parts are combined, *micromanage* means "to control in a detailed way.")

The chart below lists eight common prefixes that express number, amount, or size:

Prefix	Meaning	Example
mon-, mono-	one	monosyllable
uni-	one	unicycle
bi-, bin-	two	bicycle
tri-	three	tricornered
semi-	half, partially	semicircle
hyper-	too much	hyperactive
multi-	many, much	multivitamin
micro-	small, short	microfiber

A. Identifying Prefixes and Base Words

Underline the correct prefix in Column A to complete a word. Then match each word with its correct meaning in Column B. Write the letter of the correct meaning in the space provided. Use a dictionary if necessary.

Column A

EXAMPLE (mono-, micro-) rail _L_

1. (micro-, bi-) plane   _____
2. (multi—, uni-) talented   _____
3. (micro-, multi) chip   _____
4. (mono-, semi-) conscious   _____
5. (uni-, semi-) form   _____
6. (micro-, multi-) purpose   _____
7. (hyper-, semi-) critical   _____
8. (tri-, bi-) weekly   _____
9. (tri-, bi-) dimensional   _____
10. (micro-, mono-) molecular   _____

Column B

L. a single track for a train

A. a small device that holds information

B. having many uses

C. relating to a single molecule

D. having three dimensions

E. too severe in judgment

F. always the same; having one form

G. having many skills

H. an airplane with two sets of wings

I. only half-awake or partially aware

J. happening every two weeks

Lesson 8

Prefixes and Base Words

More Practice

B. Prefixes and Base Words in Action

For each underlined word below, draw a line between the prefix and the base word. Then write a short definition of each word using what you know about prefixes and context clues. Use a dictionary to check your answers.

EXAMPLE We were exhausted after climbing the stairs in the multi|story hotel. *several stories.*

1. Our <u>biannual</u> film festival is held in January and in July. _____

2. The team advanced to the state <u>semifinal</u> competition. _____

3. The presenter spoke in a <u>monotone</u> that bored us. _____

4. Miles injured himself by <u>hyperextending</u> his right elbow. _____

5. Javier is <u>multilingual</u>; he knows Spanish and English. _____

6. Rudy studied the <u>microorganisms</u> that live in Haven Lake. _____

C. Vocabulary Challenge

For each prefix below, provide three different base words. Then write a sentence using one of the new words.

EXAMPLE mon-, mono- *chromatic, ocular, lingual*
The monochromatic room was decorated all in white.

1. *bi-* _____, _____, _____

_____

2. *semi-* _____, _____, _____

_____

3. *hyper-* _____, _____, _____

_____

Lesson 9 # Base Words and Suffixes   *Teaching*

One way to understand a word's meaning is to break it down into its different word parts. A **base word** is a complete word that can stand alone. A **suffix** is a word part that appears at the end of a base word, altering its meaning or part of speech. Note that sometimes when a suffix is added to a base word, the base word changes slightly or loses a letter to accommodate the suffix.

For example, consider the word *describing*.

(The base word *describe* means "to convey an idea or impression.") (The suffix *-ing* indicates an ongoing or progressive action.)

describing = describe + ing.

(When the word parts are combined, *describing* means "conveying an idea.")

The chart below lists seven common suffixes and their effects on base words.

Suffix	Effect on Base Word	Examples
-s/-es	changes the number of a noun (from one to more than one)	pencil + s = pencils, diary + es = diaries
-d/-ed	changes verb tense (from present to past)	manage + d = managed, study + ed = studied
-en	changes verb tense (to past participle)	eat + en = eaten, write + en = written
-ing	changes verb tense (ongoing action)	dress + ing = dressing, describe + ing = describing
-er	changes the degree of comparison in modifiers (more but not most)	warm + er = warmer, sturdy + er = sturdier
-est	changes the degree of comparison in modifiers (the most)	long + est = longest, happy + est = happiest
-y	changes part of speech (from noun to adjective)	soap + y = soapy, fun + y = funny

A. Identifying Base Words and Suffixes

For each example, draw a line between the base word and suffix. Then choose the correct definition of the word from the options given.

1. silky   a) adjective formed from silk   b) more silk   c) past participle of silk

2. relaxed   a) progressive tense of relax   b) past participle of relax   c) past tense of relax

3. carpets   a) more than one carpet   b) adjective formed from carpet   c) past tense of carpet

4. hidden   a) progressive tense of hide   b) past participle of hide   c) past tense of hide

5. freezing   a) past tense of freeze   b) adjective formed from freeze   c) progressive tense of freeze

6. tripped   a) more than one trip   b) the most trips   c) past tense of trip

7. lovelier   a) more lovely than something b) the most lovely   c) past participle of lovely

8. belonging a) more than one belonging   b) progressive tense of belong   c) adjective formed from belong

9. cherries   a) past tense of cherry   b) past participle of cherry   c) more than one cherry

10. mightiest a) the most mighty   b) more mighty   c) progressive tense of mighty

Lesson 9 Base Words and Suffixes   *More Practice*

B. Base Words and Suffixes in Action

For each item, underline the word that correctly completes the sentence.

1. The (rockied, rocky) path led us to our camp.

2. After we had (eaten, eating) the chicken wings, we started in on the pizza.

3. I (divides, divided) the apple in two and gave a half to each child.

4. He (shocked, shocking) everyone when he got the best grade in class.

5. The two-headed chicken is the (strangest, stranger) attraction in the circus.

6. Place those five (box, boxes) on top of the table in the corner.

7. Today is much (coldest, colder) than yesterday.

8. When she opened the door, the (liveliest, lively) of the three puppies jumped into her arms.

9. They have (taked, taken) away the garbage cans from the park.

10. What are you going to do on this beautiful, (sunny, sunning) day?

C. Vocabulary Challenge

Add two suffixes to each base word to create two new words. Use these suffixes:
-s, /-es, -d/-ed, -ing, -en, -est, or *-y*. Then write a sentence using one of the new words. Remember, you may need to change the spelling of the base word.

EXAMPLE base word <u>sun</u>   new word <u>*sunny*</u>   new word <u>*sunning*</u>
            Monica was known to have a sunny personality.

1. base word <u>skate</u>   new word _____   new word _____

   _____

2. base word <u>bite</u>   new word _____   new word _____

   _____

3. base word <u>bright</u>   new word _____   new word _____

   _____

4. base word <u>milk</u>   new word _____   new word _____

   _____

5. base word <u>trick</u>   new word _____   new word _____

   _____

Lesson 10 Base Words and Suffixes

Teaching

Breaking a word down into its different parts is one way to understand the word's meaning. A **base word** is a complete word that can stand alone. A **suffix** is a word part that appears at the end of a base word. A suffix can change the word's meaning and often determines its part of speech. This lesson will focus on adjectives and adverbs formed by suffixes. Note that sometimes when a suffix is added to a base word, the base word changes slightly or loses a letter to accommodate the suffix.

For example, consider the word *pleasant.*

The base word *please,* means " to provide enjoyment."   The suffix *–ant* means "inclined to."

please + ant = pleasant

When the word parts are combined, *pleasant* means "inclined to please."

The chart below lists seven common suffixes and their meanings:

Suffix	Part of Speech	Meaning	Example
-able/-ible	adjective	inclined to, able to be	acceptable, combustible
-ant/-ent	adjective	in a specific state or condition	pleasant,different
-ful	adjective	full of	graceful
-ious/-ous	adjective	possessing; full of	gracious, joyous
-less	adverb	without; lacking	senseless
-ly	adverb	like; in a manner of	brotherly
-wise	adverb	in a manner, direction, or position	lengthwise

A. Identifying Base Words and Suffixes

Add a suffix to each base word to create a word with the meaning shown. Then write a short sentence using each new word.

EXAMPLE joy*ful*: full of happiness *Paul and Carrie's wedding was a joyful occasion.*

1. worth_____; without value _____

2. spite_____; full of anger_____

3. slant_____; diagonal direction _____

4. comfort_____; security and ease _____

5. scholar_____; like a student _____

6. agree_____; inclined to allow _____

7. fear_____; full of fear _____

8. nerv(e) _____; state of unease _____

9. vigil_____; inclined to be watchful _____

10. care_____; without care _____

Lesson 10

Base Words and Suffixes

More Practice

B. Base Words and Suffixes in Action

Suffixes: *-able/-ible, -ant/-ent, -ful, -ious/-ous, -less, -ly, -wise*

Underline ten examples in the passage that end with the suffixes listed above. Write the suffix and base word of each example. Then define each example using what you know about suffixes, base words, and context clues. Use a dictionary to check your answers.

Today our excellent staff of volunteers worked for three hours, packing boxes of food for the homeless. As always, we packed only canned goods and other items that are not perishable. This year's collection is even more remarkable than last year's. We are thankful for everyone's ambitious contribution. I am hopeful that our tireless efforts will make a difference. Finally, the less fortunate citizens in our community should be able to move forward; otherwise we fail in our mission.

1. suffix: _____ base word: _____ meaning: _____

2. suffix: _____ base word: _____ meaning: _____

3. suffix: _____ base word: _____ meaning: _____

4. suffix: _____ base word: _____ meaning: _____

5. suffix: _____ base word: _____ meaning: _____

6. suffix: _____ base word: _____ meaning: _____

7. suffix: _____ base word: _____ meaning: _____

8. suffix: _____ base word: _____ meaning: _____

9. suffix: _____ base word: _____ meaning: _____

10. suffix: _____ base word: _____ meaning: _____

C. Vocabulary Challenge

For each suffix below, provide three different base words. Then write a sentence using one of the new words.

EXAMPLE *harm, tear, thought* -ful
Giving the elderly woman flowers was a thoughtful gesture.

1. _____, _____, _____ –ly

_____

2. _____, _____, _____ –less

_____

3. _____, _____, _____ –ious, –ous

_____

Base Words and Suffixes

Teaching

A good way to approach unfamiliar words is to break them into their parts. Two important word parts are base words and suffixes. **Base words** are words that can stand alone. **Suffixes** are word parts that are added to the end of base words. Suffixes usually change the base word's part of speech.

(base word—a verb that means "to fill with wonder or surprise")

amaze + -ment = amazement

(noun suffix that means "state or quality of")   (noun that means "the state of being filled with wonder or surprise")

Study the common suffixes listed in the chart below.

Suffix	Part of Speech	Meaning	Example
-al	adjective	relating to	rental, bridal, natural
-ment	noun	state or quality of	enrichment, excitement, government
-ate	verb	to make	activate, antiquate, decorate
-fy/-ify	verb	to make	satisfy, electrify, personify
-ant	noun	one who	servant, assailant, confidant
-ways	adverb	in what manner	sideways, always, slantways
-ize	verb	to make	standardize, harmonize, magnetize, normalize
-some	adjective	likely to	awesome, meddlesome, loathsome, wearisome

A. Identifying Base Words and Suffixes

For each item, draw a line between the base word and the suffix. Then use the chart and your knowledge of word parts to predict each word's meaning. Check your predictions in a dictionary.

EXAMPLE popular/ize (verb) Meaning: *to make well-known or well-liked*

1. fearsome (adjective) meaning: _____

2. solidify (verb)   meaning: _____

3. informant (noun)   meaning: _____

4. crossways (adverb) meaning: _____

5. alienate (verb)   meaning: _____

6. brutal (adjective) meaning: _____

7. refinement (noun)   meaning: _____

8. quarrelsome (noun) meaning: _____

9. modernize (noun)   meaning: _____

10. attendant (noun)   meaning: _____

Base Words and Suffixes

More Practice

B. Base Words and Suffixes in Action

For each item, circle the suffix of the bold-faced word. Then use context clues and the chart on the previous page to predict the word's meaning. Check your predictions in a dictionary.

1. Scientists believe that a **pollutant** in Danvers Lake is killing fish.

   meaning: _____

2. Do you ever **fantasize** about being a movie star or a superhero?

   meaning: _____

3. My father is looking for **employment** as a bus driver.

   meaning: _____

4. The Olympics are a **global** event; they interest people in every country.

   meaning: _____

5. Please fold your paper **lengthways,** so it has two long columns.

   meaning: _____

6. That noisy, colorful toy is sure to **captivate** the baby.

   meaning: _____

7. Deanna says she can **customize** a computer program just for me.

   meaning: _____

8. Our club decided to **beautify** the highway by planting shrubs and flowers near it.

   meaning: _____

C. Vocabulary Challenge

Read the passage. Using context clues and the chart on the previous page, choose the correct word and circle it. You may also use a dictionary if needed.

The (defendant, combatant) and her lawyer stood up in the crowded courtroom. "I believe that you and your (sealant, assistant) tried to (justify, falsify) company records for the (enrichment, advisement) of your own bank accounts," the judge said. "Do you have anything to say in your defense?"

The woman reacted with (astonishment, assortment). "I'm innocent, Your Honor!" she insisted.

Anglo-Saxon Affixes and Base Words

Teaching

Many words we use each day come from **Anglo-Saxon** (Old English). Anglo-Saxon words often contain **affixes**—word parts that can be attached to the beginning (prefix) or end (suffix) of base words to create new words.

> prefix from Old English *fore*, meaning "in front, before, ahead of time"

fore + cast = forecast

> base word meaning "to throw or calculate"   word that means "to calculate ahead of time"

The chart shows several common affixes, along with their meanings and examples.

Affix	Type	Meaning	Example
a-	prefix	on, in; in the act or direction of	aloud
fore-	prefix	before, earlier	forewarn
over-	prefix	above, excessive	overkill
self-	prefix	oneself, automatic	self-expression
under-	prefix	beneath or below	underweight
-dom	suffix	state, position, domain, rank	kingdom
-hood	suffix	state, quality, or group	sisterhood
-ish	suffix	of, relating to, characteristic of	Spanish
-most	suffix	most, nearest to	innermost
-ship	suffix	state, quality, or group	readership

A. Vocabulary Words in Action

Add a prefix or a suffix to each base word to create a word with the meaning shown. Then write a short sentence using each new word.

1. _____-taught: learned by oneself _____

2. green_____: resembling green _____

3. _____glow: glowing _____

4. _____head: the front part of one's head _____

5. champion_____: being a champion _____

6. king_____: under a dominating factor _____

7. bottom_____: the very bottom _____

8. _____seas: abroad _____

9. _____ground: beneath the ground _____

10. brother_____: men united for a purpose _____

Lesson 12

Anglo-Saxon Affixes and Base Words

More Practice

B. Anglo-Saxon Affixes and Base Words in Action

Read each sentence below. Use context clues and your knowledge of Anglo-Saxon affixes and base words to figure out what word from the word bank belongs in each blank. Then fill in the blank.

abuzz	*overemphasize*	*self-doubt*	*neighborhood*	*topmost*
childish	*wisdom*	*underpaid*	*leadership*	*foremothers*

1. The crowd was _____ with talk of ghosts and freedom.

2. Jeremy's _____ affected his performance in the competition.

3. _____ prevails. The king must not eat oats, or he will turn into a pumpkin!

4. I placed my foot on the _____ rung of the ship's ladder, and cried: "Land, ho!"

5. "Stop acting so _____, Daruna!" she exclaimed, as Daruna stuck out her tongue for the third time.

6. Look to the stories of old, and you shall see how our _____ kept music alive.

7. As a server in a diner, Ella is _____ and overworked.

8. Darryl tends to _____ and exaggerate his accomplishments.

9. True _____ exists when you empower others, when you encourage the best in each person.

10. In our _____, people look out for each other.

C. Anglo-Saxon Word Challenge

For each Anglo-Saxon base word, add an affix to form a new word. Then write a sentence using the word.

1. _____far

_____

2. free_____

_____

3. outer_____

_____

4. _____come

_____

5. _____motivation

_____

Name _____ Date _____

 Lesson 13 # Latin Roots and Word Families   *Teaching*

Many English words are made up of word parts that come from other languages, especially Latin and Greek. These word parts are called **roots,** and their meaning is a clue to the meaning of the English word. Roots cannot stand alone, but must be combined with prefixes or suffixes. A group of words with a common root is a called a **word family.**

Latin Root	Meaning	Word Family
cred or *credit*	believe *or* trust	credible, incredible, discredit, creditable
flect or *flex*	bend	deflect, reflective, flexible, reflection
funct	perform	defunct, malfunction, nonfunctioning
fract or *frag*	break	fragment, fraction, refracting
grat or *grac*	pleasing *or* thankful	ungrateful, gratify, ingrate
later	side	bilateral, trilateral
loc or *locat*	place	locally, locale, located
var	different	variable, invariable, various, variant

The following tips can help you use roots to figure out the meaning of unfamiliar words such as *unilateral.*

- Break the word into its parts: (prefix) uni- + (root) *later* + (suffix) –al
- Think of other words you know that have the root *later,* such as *lateral* and *multilateral.* Decide the meaning that they share—"side."
- Think about the meaning of any prefixes or suffixes in the word: *uni-* means "one," and -*al* means "relating to."
- Put this information together to predict what *unilateral* means: "being one-sided."
- Check the context and a dictionary or glossary to see if your guess is correct.

A. Identifying Roots and Word Families

Underline the root of each word in Column A. Then match each word with its correct meaning in Column B. Write the letter of the correct meaning in the space provided. Use the chart to help you. You may also use a dictionary if needed.

Column A

1. dislocated _____
2. inflexible _____
3. multilateral _____
4. invariable _____
5. fragmented _____
6. malfunctioning _____
7. ingrate _____
8. credible _____
9. gratify _____
10. various _____

Column B

A. broken into pieces

B. one who is not thankful

C. not able to bend

D. capable of being believed

E. pulled out of place

F. to make pleased or satisfied

G. having many sides

H. not working

I. not able to change

J. different

Latin Roots and Word Families   *More Practice*

B. Roots and Word Families in Action

Predict the meaning of each underlined word following the steps on the previous page
and using context clues given in the sentences. Check your predictions in a dictionary.

1. Ellen is a <u>gracious</u> host—she always makes sure that the food is delicious and the decorations
   are beautiful.

   meaning: _____

2. Todd did all he could to <u>discredit</u> Ellen's story, but I believed what she said.

   meaning: _____

3. The pond was so still that I could see my face <u>reflected</u> in it.

   meaning: _____

4. My allowance is <u>variable</u>; if I do more chores, I get a larger amount.

   meaning: _____

5. My favorite store is <u>defunct</u>. Maybe another store will move into the empty space.

   meaning: _____

6. Tisha could find only a few <u>fragments</u> of the shattered plate.

   meaning: _____

C. Vocabulary Challenge

For each item, write the root shared by the two bold-faced words. Then write the
meaning of the root, using your knowledge of roots and context clues. Check
your answers in a dictionary.

> **EXAMPLE** I knew the dog would growl at me if I **transgressed,** or stepped across, the boundary.
> The scientist wanted to invent a machine that would let him **regress,** or take a step back,
> in time.
>
> root: _*gress*_ meaning: _*step*_

1. Sheri has **dental** problems—her teeth are crooked.
   A **trident** is a weapon with three spears, which are sometimes called teeth.

   root : _____ meaning: _____

2. Dr. Salcedo specializes in **prenatal** care, or taking care of babies before they are born.
   "Felicitations on your **natal** day," Edwin said, but what he really meant was "Happy birthday."

   root: _____ meaning: _____

3. There was a **palpable** chill in the air; we could really feel the cold.
   A doctor will **palpate,** or feel, a patient's sore stomach to try to find the problem.

   root: _____ meaning: _____

Greek Roots and Word Families

Teaching

A **word family** is a group of words that share the same **root**—the part of the word that gives its basic meaning. The meaning of the root, which often is Greek or Latin, can help you figure out the meaning of the English word. This chart shows some of the most common Greek roots, also called **combining forms.**

Root/Combining Form	Meaning	Examples
cosm	world *or* universe	cosmic, microcosm
graph or *gram*	write, draw, *or* record	graph, graphic, telegraph
log	word *or* study	logic, cosmology
micro	small	microsurgery, microcomputer
phon	sound	phonics, microphone
phot	light	photographer, photocopier
scop or *skept*	look at, examine	skeptic, skeptical, microscope
tel or *tele*	far, distant	telephone, telescope

The following tips can help you use roots to figure out the meaning of unfamiliar words such as *microscopic.*

- Break the word into its parts: (root) *micro* + (root) *scop* + (suffix) -ic
- Think of other words you know that have the root *scop,* such as *telescope* and *periscope.* Decide the meaning they share—"see."
- Think about the meaning of the rest of the word parts: *micro-,* "small" and *-ic,* "relating to."
- Put this information together to predict what *microscopic* means: "relating to things that are too small to see."
- Check the context of the sentence or paragraph and a dictionary to see whether your prediction is correct.

A. Roots and Word Families in Action

Use the chart above and your knowledge of word parts to match each word in Column A with its correct meaning in Column B. You may also use a dictionary if needed.

Column A

1. telescope _____

2. cosmic _____

3. microwave _____

4. photograph _____

5. telegram _____

6. logical _____

7. skeptic _____

8. microphone _____

9. telephone _____

10. cosmology _____

Column B

A. an image recorded by a camera

B. a device that carries sound over long distances

C. a person who examines things for himself or herself

D. the study of the universe

E. an oven that uses very short electromagnetic waves

F. a device that lets the user look at distant objects

G. a device that makes sound louder

H. a written message sent over a distance

I. relating to the universe

J. carefully thought out

Lesson 14

Greek Roots and Word Families

More Practice

B. Roots and Word Families in Action

Predict the meaning of each underlined word following the steps on the previous page and using context clues given in the sentences. Use a dictionary to check your answers.

1. I wish you wouldn't <u>micromanage</u> everything. You aren't responsible for every little detail!

   meaning: _____

2. Please make a <u>graph</u> that shows how much money we have raised this year and last year.

   meaning: _____

3. Sid made 30 <u>photocopies</u> of his poem to distribute to the class.

   meaning: _____

4. The astronomer wanted to create a map of the entire <u>cosmos</u>.

   meaning: _____

5. Ms. Greenberg, a writer, is working on a <u>teleplay</u> for my favorite TV show.

   meaning: _____

6. <u>Microfiber</u> fabric is often used for winter coats because it doesn't let water through.

   meaning: _____

C. Vocabulary Challenge

For each item, write the Greek root shared by the two bold-faced words. Then write the definition of the root. Use a dictionary if necessary.

> **EXAMPLE**   A **geologist** studies the earth's origin, history, and structure.
> In **geography** class, I learned how the continents formed.
>
> root: _geo_ meaning: _earth_

1. I **reclined** in the chair and enjoyed the sunshine.
   I am **inclined** to finish the project now, but Stella wants to wait.

   root: _____ meaning: _____

2. Dr. Mokwunye, a **cardiologist,** carefully listened to my heartbeat.
   He ordered a **cardiogram** to find out whether my heart was healthy.

   root: _____ meaning: _____

3. Brenda's **caustic** remarks made my face burn with shame.
   The doctor had to **cauterize,** or burn, the wound to prevent infection.

   root: _____ meaning: _____

Foreign Words in English

Teaching

Many English words have been borrowed from other languages. These words often keep the pronunciation from their original languages, so it is often hard to predict how to pronounce them. Context clues and a dictionary can help.

> **boutique** (bōō-tēk′) *noun* **1.** A small shop that specializes in selling gifts, fashionable clothes, accessories such as hats and gloves, or food to the public. **2.** A small shop within a department store or supermarket. [French, from Old French *botique,* small shop.]
>
> Pronunciation: *-tique* at the end of French words is pronounced / tēk / (rhymes with *weak*)
>
> Etymology (word origin): *boutique* is a French word

Study the words in the chart below. Pronunciations have been provided for you.

French	Spanish	Italian	Japanese	Dutch
bouquet / bō kā′ / *or* / bōō kā′/	bonanza / bə nǎn′zə /	graffiti / grə fē′te /	judo / jōō′dō /	aloof / ə-lōōf′/
chauffeur / shō′fər / *or* / shō fûr′/	guerrilla / gə rǐl′ ə /	soprano / sə prǎn′ō / *or* / sə prä′nō /	samurai / sǎm′ə-rī′/	gruesome / grōō′səm /
espionage / ěs′pē ə näzh′/	hacienda / hä′sē ěn′də /	staccato / stə-kä′tō /	tsunami / tsōō-nä′ mē /	knack / nǎk /
sabotage / sǎb′ə täzh′/	lasso / lǎs′ō / *or* / lǎ sōō′/	virtuoso / vûr chōō-ō′sō /	tycoon / tī-kōōn′/	maelstrom / māl′strəm /

A. Identifying Foreign Words

Some textbooks and magazines use simplified respellings like the ones below. For each word below, circle the letter of the correct respelling. Use the charts on this page to help you.

EXAMPLE judo a) JOOD-oh (b) JOO-doe c) joo-DOO

1. knack   a) nak   b) kuh-NAK   c) nayk
2. tycoon   a) TIKE-oon   b) TIE-koon   c) tie-KOON
3. espionage   a) ESS-pee-oh-nog   b) ESS-pee-oh-nahz   c) ess-PAY-oh-nahz
4. bonanza   a) buh-NAN-zuh   b) buh-nan-ZUH   c) bow-NON-zuh
5. staccato   a) STACK-a-toe   b) stuh-KAH-toe   c) stuh-KAH-too
6. virtuoso   a) ver-two-OH-soo   b) verch-oo-OH-soo   c) vur-choo-OH-so
7. tsunami   a) tuh-soo-NAM-ee   b) soo-NAH-mee   c) SOON-ah-me
8. aloof   a) uh-LOOF   b) ay-LOOF   c) all-OOF
9. sabotage   a) SAB-uh-tazh   b) sa-BOW-taj   c) SAH-bow-tazh
10. hacienda   a) hay-see-END-day   b) ha-SEE-en-duh   c) hah-see-EN-duh

Pronunciation Guide

ă p**a**t; oi b**oy**; ô p**aw**; th **th**in; ā p**ay**; ǐ p**i**t; ou **ou**t; th **th**is; är c**are**; ī p**ie**; ŏŏ t**oo**k; hw **wh**ich; ä f**a**ther; îr p**ier**; ōō b**oo**t; zh vi**s**ion; ě p**e**t; ŏ p**o**t; ŭ c**u**t; ə **a**bout, it**e**m; ē b**e**; ō t**oe**; ür **ur**ge; ♦ regionalism
Stress marks: ′ (primary); ′ (secondary), as in **dictionary** (dik′ shə-nĕr′ē)

Lesson 15

Foreign Words in English

More Practice

B. Foreign Words in Action

Underline the foreign word in each sentence. Use context clues to predict its meaning. Then look up the word in a dictionary and write its definition.

1. Instead of just one flower, Patricia gave me an entire bouquet.

   prediction: _____ definition: _____

2. Reading about the gruesome crime made Nate shiver in fear.

   prediction: _____ definition: _____

3. Sam certainly has a knack for cooking—dinner smells great!

   prediction: _____ definition: _____

4. It took two coats of paint to cover the graffiti scribbled on the wall.

   prediction: _____ definition: _____

5. The tycoon made her first $5 million by creating Web sites for pet owners.

   prediction: _____ definition: _____

6. The chauffeur wore a uniform and drove a shiny black car all over town.

   prediction: _____ definition: _____

C. Vocabulary Challenge

For each item, circle the foreign word or phrase. Use context clues to determine which of the three definitions is correct, and circle the letter of the correct definition. Then check the meaning and pronunciation in the dictionary.

   EXAMPLE   I won't see you before your trip, so bon voyage!
   a) see you soon b) have a good trip c) welcome back

1. "Eureka!" shouted the scientist. "I have discovered a way to turn wheat into fuel!"
   a) I have found it   b) I am frustrated   c) excuse me

2. Tara thought people would arrive at the party one by one, but instead the guests came en masse.
   a) in a car   b) in a large group   c) late

3. "Who wants to eat alfresco when it's raining out?" Dan demanded. "We will get soaked!"
   a) spaghetti   b) outdoors   c) with our fingers

Lesson 16 **Analyzing Base Words, Roots, and Affixes** *Teaching*

Base words are words that can stand alone. Other words are made up of base words or **roots** (word parts that cannot stand alone) and **affixes** (prefixes and suffixes). Breaking a difficult word into smaller parts can help you understand its meaning.

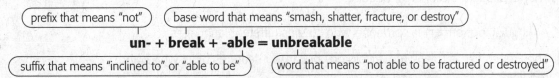

(prefix that means "not") (base word that means "smash, shatter, fracture, or destroy")

un- + break + -able = unbreakable

(suffix that means "inclined to" or "able to be") (word that means "not able to be fractured or destroyed")

Base words sometimes change spelling when combined with other word parts. If you are unsure of the spelling of a word, check a dictionary.

Study the common base words, roots, and affixes in the charts below.

Prefix	Base Word/Root	Suffix
uni- (one)	*ceive* or *cept* (take)	*-al* (relating to)
bi- (two)	*color*	*-ation, -ion, -sion* (state or quality of)
tri- (three)	*cycl* (circle *or* ring)	*-d, -ed* (changes a verb from present to past)
pre- (before)	*form*	*-er, -or* (one who does)
re- (back *or* again)	*lingu* (language)	*-ist* (one who does)
per- (throughout)	*port* (carry)	*-s* (makes a noun plural or a verb present tense)
tele- (across)	*view*	

A. Identifying Base Words, Roots, and Affixes

For each item, write the letter of the correct meaning in the blank. Use the chart above and your knowledge of word parts to help you. You may also use a dictionary if needed.

EXAMPLE tricycle __D__

1. receives _____
2. reporter _____
3. previewed _____
4. bicolor _____
5. uniform _____
6. porter _____
7. bicyclist _____
8. perceived _____
9. recycled _____
10. reformation _____

A. saw *or* understood

B. the state of being created again

C. someone who carries bags

D. a three-wheeled cycle

E. someone who gathers news

F. used again

G. having two colors

H. someone who rides a two-wheeled cycle

I. takes

J. having only one shape

K. looked at beforehand

Lesson 16 Analyzing Base Words, Roots, and Affixes   *More Practice*

B. Base Words, Roots, and Affixes in Action

For each item, circle the word that fits the sentence. Use the chart on the previous page, context clues, and your knowledge of word parts to help you. You may also use a dictionary if needed.

1. A (linguist, performer) is someone who studies different languages.

2. The French flag is (bicolored, tricolored) because it features blue, white, and red fields.

3. The science fiction movie was about (perception, teleportation), or moving people and objects from one place to another instantly.

4. Maribel is (bilingual, performed); she grew up speaking Spanish and English.

5. Our school held a (reception, previewer) so we could meet the new exchange students.

6. I can't hear you very well—I don't think the telephone's (preformed, receiver) is working.

7. The (unicyclist, formation) juggled six oranges while balancing on a single wheel.

8. Damien is a superb (performer, reporter). He can sing, dance, act, and tell jokes.

9. I always read Arlene Zuker's movie (recycling, reviews) to help me decide which films are worth seeing.

10. Can you (perceive, uniform) any difference between the two paintings?

C. Vocabulary Challenge

For each item, add affixes to the root or base word to form two new words. Then write a sentence using one of the new words. Check a dictionary to be sure that you are spelling and using the words correctly.

EXAMPLE *medi* (middle) <u>medium</u> <u>mediate</u>
My mother had to mediate the argument between my sister and me.

1. build _____ _____

   _____.

2. press _____ _____

   _____.

3. *dict* (to speak) _____ _____

   _____.

4. *divid* or *divis* (separate) _____ _____

   _____.

Lesson 17

Analyzing Base Words, Roots, and Affixes   *Teaching*

Analyzing word parts is a good way to get an idea of a word's meaning. These word parts include **base words,** which are words that can stand alone; **roots,** which are word parts that cannot stand alone; and **affixes,** which are word parts added to the beginning (prefix) or end (suffix) of base words and roots to form new words.

(prefix that means "below" or "beneath")   (root that means "dip" or "dive")

sub- + merg + -ed = submerged

(suffix that changes verb tense from present to past)   (word that means "dived beneath")

Base words sometimes change spelling when combined with other word parts. If you are unsure of the spelling of a word, check a dictionary.

Study the common roots and affixes in the charts below.

Prefix	Base Word or Root	Suffix
dis- (opposite)	*anim* (life, spirit)	*-able/-ible* (able to, wanting to, or being)
re- (back *or* again)	comfort	*-al* (relating to)
in- (not)	*domin* or *domit* (master *or* tame)	*-ate* (state or quality of)
per- (throughout)	new	*-ation, -ion, -sion* (state or quality of)
trans- (across)	*mitt* or *miss* (send)	*-d/ed* (changes verb tense from present to past)
un- (not)	seal	

A. Identifying Base Words, Roots, and Affixes

For each item, write the letter of the correct meaning in the blank. Use the chart above and your knowledge of word parts to help you. You may also use a dictionary if needed.

EXAMPLE   renew   *G*

1. domination _____
2. comforted _____
3. resealed _____
4. transmission _____
5. permitted _____
6. reanimate _____
7. mission _____
8. animal _____
9. uncomfortable _____
10. indomitable _____

A. bring back to life

B. allowed

C. calmed or soothed

D. closed up again

E. an assignment, task, or journey

F. the state of controlling something

G. make fresh again

H. uneasy, distressed, or awkward

I. a living being that is not a plant

J. sending something over a distance

K. unable to be conquered or tamed

Lesson 17

Analyzing Base Words, Roots, and Affixes

More Practice

B. Base Words, Roots, and Affixes in Action

For each item, circle the word that fits the sentence. Use the chart on the previous page, context clues, and your knowledge of word parts to help you. You may also use a dictionary if needed.

1. Fran (renewed, dismissed) her library books so she could keep them for two weeks longer.

2. Colin was very (comforted, animated) during our discussion; he talked in a loud voice and waved his arms around.

3. "Winning this war will give me (transmission, dominion) over thousands of people," said the empress. "Everyone will do as I say."

4. If it snows, the principal might (dismiss, permit) classes early.

5. Solar power is considered a (renewable, resealable) energy source because it never gets used up.

6. "You may feel some pain and (discomfort, comfortable) after the operation," Dr. Cardenas said.

7. The message on the front of the time capsule read, "Do not (permit, unseal) until 2048."

8. Those puppets may seem to be alive, but they are really (dominated, inanimate) objects.

9. "You need a(n) (transmittal, animation) form to send that package overseas," the clerk told me.

10. Do I have your (permission, renewal) to leave the room?

C. Vocabulary Challenge

For each root or base word, add affixes to form two different words. Use the prefix and suffix charts on the previous page to help you. Then write a sentence using the word. Use a dictionary to check the spelling and meaning of the word you chose.

EXAMPLE *cess* or *ced* (move or withdraw) *recede recession*
I watched the car recede into the distance as it drove away.

1. elect _____ _____

   _____

   _____

2. *migr* or *migrat* (move or travel)

   _____ _____

   _____

3. *crea* (make) _____ _____

   _____

4. connect _____ _____

   _____

5. sense _____ _____

Lesson 18 # Analyzing Roots and Affixes *Teaching*

If you see a word that you do not recognize, analyze its parts to get an idea of its meaning. Many words can be broken into **roots,** which are word parts that cannot stand alone; and **affixes,** which are word parts added to the beginning (prefix) or end (suffix) of base words and roots to form new words.

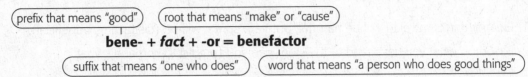

(prefix that means "good") (root that means "make" or "cause")

bene- + *fact* **+ -or = benefactor**

(suffix that means "one who does") (word that means "a person who does good things")

Base words sometimes change spelling when combined with other word parts. If you are unsure of the spelling of a word, check a dictionary.

Study the common roots and affixes in the charts below.

Prefix	Base Word or Root	Suffix
bene- (good)	*dic* or *dict* (speak *or* say)	*-ation, -ion, -sion* (state or quality of)
com- (with)	*fact* or *fic* (make *or* cause)	*-d, ed* (changes verb tense from present to past)
contra- (against)	*mand* or *mend* (entrust *or* order)	*-er, -or* (one who does)
dis- (opposite)	*put* (think)	*-ial* (relating to)
inter- (between)	*rupt* (break)	*-ing* (indicates ongoing action)
pre- (before)	*tract* (pull)	*-ment* (state or quality of)
re- (back *or* again)		*-s* (makes a noun plural or a verb present tense)

A. Identifying Roots and Affixes

For each item, write the letter of the correct meaning in the blank. Use the chart above and your knowledge of word parts to help you. You may also use a dictionary if needed.

EXAMPLE distract *C*

1. command _____
2. diction _____
3. dispute _____
4. retract _____
5. prediction _____
6. computed _____
7. disruption _____
8. recommendation _____
9. contradicted _____
10. computer _____

A. something that stops or blocks the progress of something else

B. said the opposite

C. to pull attention away from something

D. calculated

E. clearness in speaking or writing

F. to pull back

G. a machine that does calculations

H. a lack of agreement

I. a suggestion that something be done

J. order

K. a guess about what will happen; a foretelling

Name _____   Date _____

Analyzing Roots and Affixes

B. Roots and Affixes in Action

For each item, circle the word that fits the sentence. Use the chart on the previous page, context clues, and your knowledge of word parts to help you. You may also use a dictionary if needed.

1. Eleanor thinks my plan will be harmful, but I am sure it will be (distracting, beneficial).

2. Based on what you have read of the story, can you (predict, command) what happens next?

3. Please don't (dispute, interrupt) me. I will be glad to listen to what you have to say once I finish speaking.

4. The general (commanded, factored) an army of 15,000.

5. There's no need to take (dictation, computation)—you don't have to write down everything I say.

6. The minister said the (benediction, faction), or blessing, at the end of the service.

7. The twins are always (commending, contradicting) each other. Jenna says the opposite of whatever Shelley says.

8. If my (computations, interruptions) are correct, you owe me $3.82.

9. Having a squawking parrot in our classroom is certainly a (retraction, distraction). Nobody can concentrate because of all the noise.

10. Albert received many awards and (commendations, disruptions) for his act of bravery.

C. Vocabulary Challenge

For each root, add affixes to form two different words. Use your knowledge of affixes to help you. Then write a sentence using one of the words. Use a dictionary to check the spelling and meaning of the word you chose.

> **EXAMPLE**   *sci* (know)   <u>science   scientist</u>
> <u>The scientist searched for a way to cure the deadly disease.</u>

1. *solv* or *solut* (loosen *or* set free) _____   _____

   _____

2. *psych* (mind *or* soul) _____   _____

   _____

3. *ped* (foot) _____   _____

   _____

4. *aud* (hear) _____   _____

   _____

5. *pop* (people) _____   _____

   _____

Lesson 19

Specialized Vocabulary

Teaching

People who work in many different fields, from law to the different sciences to manufacturing, use particular terms and names called **specialized vocabulary.** Use what you know about **context** (other information in the sentence) and word parts to help you figure out the meaning of specialized vocabulary.

> The hospital uses a strong **disinfectant** to kill germs.

This sentence tells you what a disinfectant is—something used to kill germs. Knowing that the prefix *dis-* means "not" or "lack of" and the word *infect* means "to make sick" or "to transmit a disease to" can also help you determine the meaning of *disinfectant.*

A. Identifying Specialized Vocabulary

Underline the information in each sentence that is a clue to the meaning of the bold-faced word. Think about whether you know any words with the same word root as the bold-faced word. Then write the definition of the word on the line. Check your definitions in a dictionary.

1. The flu is highly **contagious**—it spreads easily from person to person.

   meaning: _____

2. David is **allergic** to flowers. He sneezes and his eyes get watery when he is near them.

   meaning: _____

3. Scientists have worked for decades to find a **remedy,** or cure, for the common cold.

   meaning: _____

4. Nobody likes getting an **injection**, which is medication delivered by way of a needle in the skin.

   meaning: _____

5. Louis Pasteur experimented with **vaccinations** using injections of dead or weakened germs.

   meaning: _____

6. Smoking interferes with **respiration.** Heavy smokers often have difficulty breathing.

   meaning: _____

7. The **incubation** period for signs of illness to appear is about four days.

   meaning: _____

8. Humans need **vitamins.** These substances in nutritious foods help keep the body functioning.

   meaning: _____

9. People with severe infectious diseases are sometimes put in **quarantine.** This isolation from others can prevent a disease from spreading.

   meaning: _____

10. Certain medicines can be ordered only by **prescription,** meaning a doctor's written order for medicine.

    meaning: _____

Specialized Vocabulary

More Practice

B. Specialized Vocabulary in Action

Use your knowledge of context clues and word parts to predict the meaning of each bold-faced word. Write your predictions on the lines below. Check your predictions in a dictionary.

Nate visited his uncle, a **surgeon**—a doctor who performs operations—at the hospital. Nate waited in **admittance,** which is where sick people first enter the hospital. He heard a man complain of **abdominal** pain, or pain in the stomach. After performing several tests, the doctor **diagnosed,** or identified, the man's illness. She told the man he would need an **appendectomy;** this means that a part of his body called the **appendix** would need to be removed by a surgeon.

A nurse told Nate that all the **instruments,** or tools, a surgeon uses must be cleaned to remove all germs or bacteria. This process is called **sterilizing,** and it keeps the instruments **sanitary,** or clean. The nurse said that germs are **microscopic,** so tiny they can be seen only under a microscope.

1. _____   6. _____

2. _____   7. _____

3. _____   8. _____

4. _____   9. _____

5. _____   10. _____

C. Vocabulary Challenge

For each item, figure out the meaning of the bold-faced word. Write that meaning on the line, and then write a sentence of your own that uses the same word. Use context clues, your knowledge of word parts, and a dictionary to help you.

1. Ed felt sick and **feverish,** so he stayed home from school.

   meaning: _____ sentence: _____

2. If you **fracture** your wrist, you will probably need to wear a cast for a few weeks.

   meaning: _____ sentence: _____

3. Having a bad cold or the flu may make you feel some pain or **discomfort.**

   meaning: _____ sentence: _____

4. Samantha is not **infectious,** so we can visit her without worrying about getting sick.

   meaning: _____ sentence: _____

Lesson 20

Specialized Vocabulary

Teaching

The **specialized vocabulary,** or specific group of words, people use in talking about sports may be unfamiliar. Sometimes looking for context clues can help you understand such a word. Breaking the word into parts may also help you learn its meaning.

> **Cross-training** allows an athlete to perfect many different skills.

- To determine the meaning of *cross-training,* think about the **context,** or words and phrases around the word. Cross-training is something that athletes do, and it lets them get better at many kinds of skills.

- Break the word into its parts: *training* is getting more practice or experience at something, and cross often means "across" or "combining the qualities of two or more things."

- Figure out that *cross-training* must mean "to practice different sports and exercises." Check your prediction in a dictionary.

A. Identifying Specialized Vocabulary

Underline the words or phrases that help you figure out the meaning of the bold-faced word. Then use context clues and your knowledge of word parts to determine the meaning of the bold-faced words. Check your predictions in a dictionary.

1. Which part of the **triathlon** is your favorite—swimming, bicycling, or running?

2. I thought he was going to **fumble** the football, but he caught the ball even though he was hit hard.

3. I can swim the **backstroke** all the way across the pool.

4. When I tore a ligament in my knee playing softball, my mother took me to an **orthopedic surgeon.**

5. I'm going to cheer for the players on Ally's team. Are you going to **root** for them too?

6. Both teams depend on the **referee** to enforce the rules of the game.

7. Tara tipped the baseball over the catcher's head and into the **backstop.**

8. Bouncing a ball doesn't seem that difficult, but basketball players practice their **dribble** for hours.

9. Adrienne got to serve again because the tennis ball was called a **let** when it hit the top of the net.

10. A golf game is measured in how many **strokes** you take—in other words, how many times you hit the ball.

Name _____ Date _____

Specialized Vocabulary

More Practice

B. Vocabulary Words in Action

Read the paragraph. Then use context clues and your knowledge of word parts to determine the meaning of the bold-faced words and phrases. Write a short meaning of each word. Check your predictions in a dictionary.

"I have been the coach of this baseball team for three years, and we have never needed a **pregame** talk like this one. Before we go out there, I want to be sure that you all show good **sportsmanship** instead of the complaining, arguing, and bad behavior I saw and heard in our last game. The **umpire** is there to enforce the rules, so be respectful. Even if you are the best **hitter** or **fielder** on the team and we need you to win, I will **bench** you if I see you acting childishly and **talking trash.** Every time we play, there are **fans**—including your parents, brothers, sisters, and friends—sitting in the **bleachers** and watching your performance. Are you ready to make them proud? Then get **warmed up** and get out there!"

1. _____   6. _____

2. _____   7. _____

3. _____   8. _____

4. _____   9. _____

5. _____   10. _____

C. Vocabulary Challenge

For each item, figure out the meaning of the bold-faced word. Write that meaning on the line, and then write a sentence of your own that uses the same word. Use context clues, your knowledge of word parts, and a dictionary to help you.

1. We were **demolished** in our last game. In fact, we lost 32 to 2.

   meaning: _____ sentence: _____

2. An effective **strategy,** or plan, is often the key to winning a game.

   meaning: _____ sentence: _____

3. **Drills** and other types of practice exercises can make you a better athlete.

   meaning: _____ sentence: _____

4. Running requires **stamina,** that is, endurance, as well as speed.

   meaning: _____ sentence: _____

Specialized Vocabulary

Lesson 21

People who work in or study special areas of knowledge use a specific group of words, or **specialized vocabulary,** in talking about their subjects. For example, you might read the following sentence in an article about science.

> Basalt rock has a greater **density,** meaning thickness or closeness of particles, than limestone.

Look at the word's **context** (the words and sentences around it) to help you figure out its meaning. Breaking the unfamiliar word into its parts can also help.

- To figure out the meaning of density, look for words such as *or, that is, in other words,* or *meaning,* that signal context clues.

- Think about words you know that have similar word roots or base words, such as "dense."

- Figure out that *density* means "thickness or closeness of particles."

A. Identifying Specialized Vocabulary

Underline the words or phrases that help you figure out the meaning of the bold-faced word or phrase. Then predict the meaning of the bold-faced word. Check your predictions in a dictionary.

1. **Wildlife** such as deer, owls, mice, and bears live in these woods.

    meaning: _____

2. Carolus Linnaeus was the first person to **classify** plants and animals scientifically, or arrange them in categories.

    meaning: _____

3. The wheat field was so **saturated** with rainwater after the storm that the wheat would not grow.

    meaning: _____

4. Humans can see only a certain **spectrum,** or range, of light.

    meaning: _____

5. Some new medicines have a variety of **applications;** that is, they are used to treat many illnesses.

    meaning: _____

6. There are more white tigers in **captivity,** living in zoos or circuses, than there are in the wild.

    meaning: _____

7. Have you gathered all the **data** you need, or do you have to find more information?

    meaning: _____

8. Snow leopards are **endangered.** There are so few of them left that they may die out.

    meaning: _____

9. A **geologist** studies rocks to find out more about the earth's history.

    meaning: _____

10. Scientists take extra safety precautions when working with **toxic,** or poisonous, chemicals.

    meaning: _____

Name _____ Date _____

Specialized Vocabulary

More Practice

B. Specialized Vocabulary in Action

Read the paragraph. Then use context clues and your knowledge of word parts to determine the meaning of the bold-faced words and phrases. Write a short meaning of each word. Check your predictions in a dictionary.

    For my science project, I decided to **observe,** or pay careful attention to, what was going on in my own community. **Pollution**—impurities in the environment—has affected nearby Edinboro Lake. Many **species,** or types, of plants and animals can no longer be found there. Sometimes animals and plants can get used to a new situation like pollution in the water. This process is called **adaptation.** However, when chemicals **contaminate** the water, poisoned wildlife often dies. The plants and animals of Edinboro Lake are an **ecosystem.** In other words, they are all connected. If pollution in the lake affects **algae** and other simple plants, then **carp** and other fish will eventually be affected. Then the **predators,** animals that eat other animals, will suffer as well. People in Edinboro need to find an **equilibrium,** or balance, between humans and the environment.

1. _____   6. _____

2. _____   7. _____

3. _____   8. _____

4. _____   9. _____

5. _____   10. _____

C. Vocabulary Challenge

For each item, figure out the meaning of the bold-faced word. Write that meaning on the line, and then write a sentence of your own that uses the same word. Use context clues, your knowledge of word parts, and a dictionary to help you.

1. To find out the current temperature, check a **thermometer.**

    meaning: _____ sentence: _____

2. **Botany**—the science of studying plants—is an interesting career choice.

    meaning: _____ sentence: _____

3. Dr. Jenkins studies whales, fish, and other **undersea** life.

    meaning: _____ sentence: _____

4. The **meteorite,** an object that fell to earth from space, weighed 13 pounds.

    meaning: _____ sentence: _____

Lesson 22 # Words with Multiple Meanings   *Teaching*

Many English words have more than one meaning. Paying attention to context clues can help you figure out which meaning of the word applies in a particular sentence. The word *cast*, for example, has the following meanings:

1. to throw something, especially a light object such as a fishing line

2. to throw with great force

3. to assign one or more roles in a play or film

4. the group of actors in a play or film

5. a hard bandage made of gauze and plaster put on an injured part of the body to keep it still while it is healing

Notice how the word is used in the following sentences.

The fisherman **cast** his line again and again. (meaning 1)

Everyone in the **cast** was excellent, especially the lead actress. (meaning 4)

The **cast** on my arm is heavy and itchy. (meaning 5)

A. Identifying Multiple Meanings

Read the multiple meanings of the two words given below. Then read each sentence and write the letter of the correct meaning of the italicized word in the blank.

free

A. costing nothing

B. liberal or generous

C. without restriction

D. unoccupied

E. to release

trip

F. a journey or voyage somewhere

G. to stumble

H. a quick, light step

I. to release a trigger or switch

J. to make a mistake (usually used with *up*)

_____ 1. Since Ralph won a million dollars, he has been very *free* with his money.

_____ 2. Be careful, or you will *trip* up on that last question on the test!

_____ 3. Jeanette was determined to *free* the bird from its cage.

_____ 4. We watched the flower girl *trip* happily down the aisle at the wedding.

_____ 5. That parking space is *free*—nobody is in it.

_____ 6. This is Shana's first *trip* to New Jersey.

_____ 7. The sample was *free;* I didn't have to pay for it.

_____ 8. Be sure not to *trip* on that icy sidewalk.

_____ 9. You are *free* to select whichever dessert you like.

_____ 10. If you *trip* the switch, the alarm will go off.

Lesson 22 **Words with Multiple Meanings** *More Practice*

B. Multiple Meanings in Action

Complete each sentence with one of the two words given below. Then write the letter of the correct meaning of the word in the box.

start

A. to begin or set out

B. the beginning of something

C. to move suddenly without meaning to

D. to play in the beginning lineup of a game

E. to found or establish

drive

F. to push forward

G. to guide or control a car or other vehicle

H. a trip or journey in a vehicle

I. a road or street

J. to hit a ball forcefully

1. Melinda wants to _____ her own dog-walking business. ☐

2. Every night the cowboys _____ the cattle into the corral. ☐

3. The loud noise made Alex _____. ☐

4. I knew we would win the baseball game if I could _____ the ball into left field. ☐

5. Does the avenue or the _____ lead to your house? ☐

6. Tamara will _____ her trip tomorrow morning. ☐

7. The coach decided that Ted would _____ in the next game. ☐

8. My brother loves to _____ that rusty old car of his all over the place. ☐

9. The twins will take a long _____ in the country this afternoon. ☐

10. I knew from the _____ that this might be a problem. ☐

C. Vocabulary Challenge

Circle the word from the list that makes sense in both sentences. Use a dictionary if needed.

1. field / mark / park / store

   My dog loves to play in the _____.

   _____ your car on the side of the road.

2. fire / jump / stove / clean

   Please put an extra log on the _____.

   The manager decided to _____ the worker.

3. coat / order / dress / safe

   Karyn wore a long blue _____.

   It took her a while to _____ and get ready.

4. turn / man / groom / comb

   Marvin took a moment to comb his hair and _____ himself.

   The bride and _____ were late to their own wedding!

5. ask / cat / stuff / hound

   The _____ that lives next door barks and howls all night.

   Even if you bother and _____ me, I won't answer your questions!

Lesson 23

Synonyms

Words that are similar in meaning are called **synonyms.** These words have the same or almost the same dictionary definition, or **denotation.** However, they have different **connotations,** or ideas and feelings associated with them.

Toni **strolled** to the store to get decorations for the party.

Toni **dashed** to the store to get decorations for the party.

Both of the above sentences tell you that Toni went to the store. However, in the first sentence, she is taking her time; in the second sentence, she is in a rush!

Using a thesaurus (a reference book that lists synonyms) can help you choose the word that best expresses what you want to say.

A. Identifying Synonyms

Choose the synonym for each bold-faced word. Use a thesaurus if necessary.

1. "I am **baffled** by this mystery," said the detective.
   unfinished/confused/thoughtful

2. Javier is a talented proofreader; his **accuracy** is amazing.
   preciseness/confusion/activity

3. Getting an "A" on the test made me **jubilant.**
   surprised/disbelieving/overjoyed

4. Louisa hoped that bell-bottom jeans were just a **fad** that would soon be over.
   trend/clothing/requirement

5. My little sister can **mimic** the weird noises our cat makes—she sounds just like Snowball.
   predict/mine/imitate

6. Dan was **visibly** embarrassed by our teacher's praise. He turned bright red!
   clearly/slightly/never

7. The weather is **wretched** today. Can't you hear the rain pounding on the roof?
   changeable/horrible/surprising

8. My **willful** brother always does the opposite of what he is told.
   wild/older/stubborn

9. We plan to **expand** the club from 15 members to 30.
   enlarge/cancel/exit

10. The good news left me filled with **glee.**
    shock/sadness/joy

Synonyms

Lesson 23

More Practice

B. Synonyms in Action

mature—full-grown, ripe, responsible, developed, payable

sink—submerge, slump, worsen

thin—slender, watered-down, skimpy, flimsy

Replace each use of *mature, sink,* and *thin* with the synonym that best fits the sentence. Use context clues to help you. You may also use a thesaurus or dictionary if needed.

1. In just a few weeks, the fruit on the tree will be **mature** and ready to pick. _____

2. The bad news made me **sink** in my chair. _____

3. Giraffes have long, **thin** legs, but they are strong animals. _____

4. The savings bond I bought at the bank will be **mature** in five years. _____

5. Hitting an iceberg caused the ship to **sink.** _____

6. The paint we are using for our house is rather **thin;** some of the old color may show

   through it. _____

7. Taking a CPR class made Mike feel very **mature** because he would be able to take care

   of others. _____

8. You will do anything to **sink** his chances of winning, won't you? _____

9. Brad's shirt was made of **thin** material that didn't keep out the rain. _____

10. Lion cubs are small, but a **mature** lion can weigh up to 500 pounds. _____

C. Vocabulary Challenge

Circle the synonym that best completes each sentence. Use a dictionary or thesaurus if needed.

1. My mother was so furious that she (glared, glanced, gazed) at me for a minute before she started speaking.

2. This is a(n) (complicated, fancy, imaginative) problem; it will take time to figure out.

3. We have a (few, rare, sporadic) details to work out before we end the meeting.

4. The (stench, stink, smell) of the flowers was lovely.

5. (Chat, Speak, Whisper) the secret in my ear—I don't want anyone else to hear it.

Antonyms

Lesson 24

Antonyms are words that have opposite or nearly opposite meanings. You can sometimes figure out the meaning of an unfamiliar word in a sentence when its antonym appears in the same sentence.

> George *loves* cauliflower, but he *abhors* broccoli.

You can figure out from the sentence (especially the word *but*) that *abhors* has roughly the same meaning as *hates* or *despises.*

A thesaurus—a reference book that lists synonyms—often lists antonyms as well.

A. Antonyms in Action

Revise each item to make sense by replacing the bold-faced word or phrase with an antonym from the list below. Use a thesaurus or dictionary if needed.

flustered	despite	improvising	harmony	neutral
industrious	exaggerates	cheered	bleak	full

1. Cameron was **ravenous** after eating three pieces of cheesecake. _____

2. Eddie was **calm** when he tripped in front of everyone. _____

3. The landscape looked **bright,** with leafless trees and threatening clouds. _____

4. Our dog is lonely **because of** our three friendly cats. _____

5. Colleen always **understates** her stories; once she told us that she saw a four-inch-long

   cockroach in the cafeteria. _____

6. Brad insists on **rehearsing** his scenes in the school play, ignoring the script and making up

   his own dialogue. _____

7. The members of the committee were in complete **conflict;** they all voted to make the school

   paper a weekly publication. _____

8. Matt was so proud of Sue's game-winning goal that he **jeered** louder than

   any other fan. _____

9. I hate drab, **primary** colors; I like to wear bright blue and green and

   red clothes. _____

10. Mary is so **lazy** that she manages to get straight A's while she participates in lots

    of activities. _____

Lesson 24 Antonyms

B. Vocabulary Words in Action

For each sentence, circle the antonym for the bold-faced word. Use the antonym to help you predict the meaning of the bold-faced word, and write your prediction on the line. Check your predictions in a dictionary.

1. The twins have different tastes: Chris craves **novelty,** but Craig likes routine.

   meaning: _____.

2. Roberto left as soon as the movie ended, but Joshua **lingered** to read the credits.

   meaning: _____

3. Lydia's **melancholy** turned to happiness when she learned that she had earned an A on the math test.

   meaning: _____

4. After Roy conquered the **obstacle** of fear, there was nothing to stop him from learning to fly a plane.

   meaning: _____

5. Steve lifted the **massive** oak table without any trouble, yet he dropped the lightweight plastic lamp.

   meaning: _____

6. Are you planning to **pout** all day about being grounded, or do you think you can cheer up?

   meaning: _____

C. Vocabulary Challenge

For each item, write at least two antonyms for the bold-faced word. Then use one of the antonyms in a sentence. Use a dictionary or thesaurus if needed.

1. **shy** antonyms: _____ _____

   sentence: _____

2. **frantic** antonyms: _____ _____

   sentence: _____

3. **whisper** antonyms: _____ _____

   sentence: _____

Denotation and Connotation

Teaching

A word's **denotation** is its dictionary definition. A word can also make people feel or think a certain way. These feelings and ideas are the **connotations** of a word. Words with the same meaning can have different "shades of meaning"—that is, they can be understood differently.

Positive connotation: What a *fragrance* that perfume has! That's quite an aroma. (a pleasant, appealing smell)

Neutral connotation: What a *smell* that perfume has!

Negative connotation: What a *stink* that perfume has! That's quite a *stench*. (an unpleasant, disgusting smell)

Be sure that the words you use have the right connotation as well as the right denotation.

A. Identifying Positive and Negative Connotations

Each pair of phrases includes synonyms with different connotations. Put a **+** sign next to the one with a positive connotation and a **—** sign next to the one with a negative connotation. Use a dictionary or thesaurus if needed.

1. an aggressive athlete ___

   a pushy athlete ___

2. an arrogant statement ___

   a confident statement ___

3. known for her cleverness ___

   known for her cunning ___

4. a slender dancer ___

   a scrawny dancer ___

5. a rowdy crowd ___

   a lively crowd ___

6. pampered his pets ___

   coddled his pets ___

7. an overprotective mother ___

   a cautious mother ___

8. a colorful sweater ___

   a gaudy sweater ___

9. showed persistence ___

   showed stubbornness ___

10. spent time making small talk ___

    spent time chattering ___

Denotation and Connotation

B. Connotations in Action

You are an advertising copywriter for a travel agency. Circle the words and phrases in the paragraph that have a positive connotation. Use a dictionary or thesaurus if needed.

Come to Utopia Island!

We want you to visit our (boring, tranquil) island and its (unchanging, monotonous) beaches. When you arrive, hotel staffers in (exotic, bizarre) costumes will bring you (aromatic, stinky) foods that are native to the region. Visit our marketplaces to (invest your money in, squander your money on) our famous (trinkets, collectibles). You are welcome to wear (casual, sloppy) clothes during the day. If you wish, you may change into (fussier, more elaborate) clothing at night. All this fun can be yours for an (affordable, cheap) price. Ask your travel agent today why Utopia Island is the most (popular, commonplace) vacation destination in the world!

C. Vocabulary Challenge

Replace each word with a synonym that has a positive connotation. Then write a sentence using the synonym correctly. Use a dictionary or thesaurus if needed.

1. reckless _____

_____

2. flashy _____

_____

3. show-off _____

_____

4. slick _____

_____

5. know-it-all _____

_____

Lesson 26 Using a Thesaurus   *Teaching*

Many English words are **synonyms,** or have similar meanings. To find the word
that expresses exactly what you want to say, look in a **thesaurus,** or reference
book of synonyms. A thesaurus entry will tell you the spelling, part of speech, and
meaning of a word and its synonyms. Some thesauruses also include **antonyms,**
or words with opposite meanings. To locate a word in a thesaurus, look in the
upper corners of the page for the **guide words,** or first and last words on the page.
Words that come between those words in alphabetical order will be on that page.

hanger-on   **harbor**

Guide words—first and last words on the page

happy *adjective* **1. fortunate, lucky, providential** It was a happy coincidence
that we found you here. **2. bright, cheerful, lighthearted, sunny** Derek always
has a happy expression on his face. **3. content, fulfilled, satisfied** I am happy
with the books I bought. **4. cheery, glad, joyous** Have a happy holiday!
5. delighted, pleased We would be happy to go with you. **Antonyms:**
disappointed, distressed, gloomy, glum, miserable, unhappy, unlucky

Thesaurus entry for *happy*

Part of speech

Definitions that distinguish the synonyms,
often with example sentences

Synonyms, may be presented in alphabetical order

A. Understanding Thesaurus Entries

Answer each question by using a thesaurus to look up entries for *fly* and *following.*

1. What two guide words are on the same page as *happy?* _____

2. How many parts of speech are given for *happy?* _____

3. In what order are the synonyms given for the first definition of *happy?* _____

4. How many synonyms are given for the second definition of *happy?* _____

5. What is the purpose of the sample sentences? _____

6. What relationship do the words *glad* and *joyous* have to each other? _____

7. Which entry would you expect to find on this same page: *have, hapless,* or *hazard?* _____

8. What part of speech is *cheery?* _____

9. What relationship do *disappointed* and *distressed* have to *happy?* _____

10. What relation does the word *sunny* have to *happy?* _____

Name _____ Date _____

Using a Thesaurus

More Practice

B. Thesaurus Entries in Action

Use the thesaurus entries here to choose a more precise synonym to replace each underlined word. (For most items, more than one correct answer is possible.) Write each synonym in the space provided.

> **challenge** *noun* **1. dare, defiance** Lauren accepted Austin's challenge to a rematch on the tennis court. **2. difficulty, problem, struggle** My cousin enjoys the challenges of rock climbing. *verb* **1. summon, invite, call out, provoke** Sam challenged Michelle to a game of chess after school. **2. dispute** I challenged my mother's decision not to let me go to the dance. **3. stimulate, spur, animate, test** Putting the new jigsaw puzzle together challenged us for several hours.
>
> **stir** *verb* **1. mix, blend, fuse, merge** Stir two egg whites into the cake batter. **2. budge, move** The slight breeze stirred the tall grass. **3. rouse, awaken** My sleepy brother did not stir when I poked him in the shoulder. **4. kindle, raise** A powerful speech is sure to stir the emotions of the crowd. *noun* **commotion, disturbance, uproar** Deanna created quite a stir when she wore a purple plaid cowboy hat to school.

1. After the election, the losing candidate decided to <u>challenge</u> the results. _____

2. Did anyone in the cabin <u>stir</u> when you told them that breakfast was ready, or are they all still sleeping? _____

3. Hearing about the insult was sure to <u>stir</u> Bryan's anger. _____

4. Saving for college while working part-time was a real <u>challenge</u> for Sam. _____

5. Did your dramatic entrance cause a <u>stir</u>, or did people just ignore you? _____

6. A strong wind will <u>stir</u> the branches on that pine tree. _____

7. Your <u>challenge</u> doesn't scare me; after all, I am the checkers champion of Selma Street.

   _____

8. Doing word problems can really <u>challenge</u> my brain. _____

9. Did my incredible new plan <u>stir</u> your interest? _____

10. <u>Stir</u> the mixture with a spoon to make sure the ingredients are blended. _____

C. Vocabulary Challenge

Review the thesaurus entry for *challenge* in Exercise B. Write four sentences, illustrating different definitions of the word.

1. _____

2. _____

3. _____

4. _____

Lesson 27 ## Idioms   *Teaching*

An **idiom** is a phrase that has a special meaning different from the meanings of the individual words. Notice how the idiom *button your lip* efficiently conveys the idea of being quiet.

Just **button your lip** about the surprise party—it's a secret.

Just **keep quiet** about the surprise party—it's a secret.

The chart below lists some common idioms and their meanings.

Idiom	Meaning
a green thumb	skill at growing plants
blow the whistle	report bad behavior
cut it out	stop it
from the horse's mouth	from a knowledgeable source
hold one's tongue	keep quiet
in hot water	in trouble
in one's hair	bothersome
in the same boat	in the same situation
lend a hand	help
see eye to eye	share the same viewpoint or opinion

A. Identifying Idioms

Complete each sentence using an idiom from the chart. Each idiom is used only once. You may need to adjust verb tenses or make other grammatical changes so that the idiom fits the sentence. Use a dictionary if needed.

1. If you aren't busy, can you _____ by decorating the gym for the dance?

2. Jim really has _____; he can make any plant grow anywhere.

3. My pesky little sister is always _____. I wish she would find someone else to bother.

4. You are really bothering me! _____ this instant!

5. Frieda will _____ on us if we play baseball in the house—it's not allowed.

6. Luke found it hard to _____. He wanted to tell the secret.

7. Cisley and I began the meeting in disagreement, but after a few minutes we

    _____.

8. Of course my information is accurate—I got it _____!

9. Both of us need help with this problem, so we are _____.

10. Hannah will be _____ if she borrows Al's bike without permission. He will be furious!

Lesson 27 **Idioms**

More Practice

B. Idioms in Action

Find ten idioms in the following e-mail message. Write each idiom and then work with a partner to define them. Use a dictionary if needed.

Hey Becky,

You will never believe what happened to me. You know that I have a sweet tooth. Well, yesterday I found a big cake in the kitchen and flipped my lid. I was hungry enough to eat a horse! I ate just one tiny slice of cake, but it upset the whole apple cart. My mother runs a tight ship, so she really read me the riot act. "You have been living the life of Riley for too long," she said. "It's time to shape up or ship out!" Then she clipped my wings—I'm not allowed to watch TV for a week! My plans to watch my favorite show have gone up in smoke.

Charlene

1. idiom: _____ meaning: _____

2. idiom: _____ meaning: _____

3. idiom: _____ meaning: _____

4. idiom: _____ meaning: _____

5. idiom: _____ meaning: _____

6. idiom: _____ meaning: _____

7. idiom: _____ meaning: _____

8. idiom: _____ meaning: _____

9. idiom: _____ meaning: _____

10. idiom: _____ meaning: _____

C. Vocabulary Challenge

Work with a partner to rewrite each sentence, replacing each incorrect idiom with a correct one. Then define the correct idiom. Use a dictionary if needed.

1. Dee has a good head on her neck. You can always trust her to do the right thing.

   idiom and definition: _____ _____

2. I know just what you're planning. I can read you like a newspaper!

   idiom and definition: _____ _____

3. There's nothing we can do about it, so don't cry over spilled coffee.

   idiom and definition: _____ _____

4. César really pulled the wool over my head. I didn't know what he was planning.

   idiom and definition: _____ _____

Name _____ Date _____

Similes and Metaphors

Teaching

You can paint strong word pictures by comparing two things that share some qualities. A **simile** is a comparison of two things that have some quality in common. A simile contains a word such as *like, as, resembles,* or *than.* A **metaphor** is a comparison of two things that does not use *like, as, resembles,* or *than.* Instead, it states that one thing actually is something else.

When my brother makes dinner, the kitchen looks **like** a battleground. *(simile)*

The sink, filled with dirty dishes, is as crowded and messy **as** a junkyard. *(simile)*

The countertops are a nightmare of stains, spills, and potato peelings. *(metaphor)*

Comparison	Characteristics	Things Compared
Simile	With *like, as, resembles,* or *than*	kitchen / battleground; sink / junkyard
Metaphor	Without *like, as, resembles,* or *than*	countertops / nightmare

A. Identifying Similes and Metaphors

Underline the two items being compared in each sentence. Then write **S** if the comparison is a simile and **M** if it is a metaphor.

_____ 1. The rain felt like small kisses on Rosemary's face.

_____ 2. The moon was a ball of green cheese.

_____ 3. My cousin's baby is a perpetual motion machine.

_____ 4. When Evan blushes, his round face resembles a stop sign.

_____ 5. The news was more shocking than a thousand volts of electricity.

_____ 6. "An increase in my allowance is as necessary as carrying water in the desert," Sarah argued.

_____ 7. When he slam-dunks a basketball, Rich is a pouncing leopard.

_____ 8. The fabric was darker than a moonless night.

_____ 9. The audience watching the movie was like a zooful of noisy animals.

_____ 10. An ocean of clothes tumbled out of the closet when I opened it.

Similes and Metaphors

Lesson 28

More Practice

B. Similes and Metaphors in Action

Identify each sentence as a simile or a metaphor. Then explain the meaning of the comparison.

1. The classroom was a hive of worker bees. (simile / metaphor)

    meaning: _____

2. Traveling to other countries is like trying on other lives. (simile / metaphor)

    meaning: _____

3. Getting my little sister dressed for school is more complicated than a rocket launch. (simile / metaphor)

    meaning: _____

4. My grandfather's hands are roadmaps of wrinkles. (simile / metaphor)

    meaning: _____

5. The seven-layer sandwich resembled a skyscraper. (simile / metaphor)

    meaning: _____

6. The news was as unpleasant as a dose of cough medicine. (simile / metaphor)

    meaning: _____

7. The bathrobe was softer than a puppy's fur. (simile / metaphor)

    meaning: _____

8. When it comes to keeping secrets, Harry is a chattering parrot. (simile / metaphor)

    meaning: _____

9. "That pile of dirty laundry is a science experiment," my mother complained. (simile / metaphor)

    meaning: _____

10. My plan to raise money for the French club turned out to be as popular as a sardine-and-cinnamon pizza. (simile / metaphor)

    meaning: _____

C. Vocabulary Challenge

Complete each sentence by writing a simile or metaphor as indicated. Then write the meaning of your comparison.

1. **Metaphor:** Our basketball team is _____

    meaning: _____

2. **Metaphor:** The spelling bee was _____

    meaning: _____

3. **Simile:** Uncle Steve's chocolate cake tastes _____

    meaning: _____

4. **Simile:** That soccer uniform smells _____

    meaning: _____

5. **Metaphor:** Summer is _____

    meaning: _____

Lesson 29

Compound Words

Teaching

A **compound word** is two or more words joined to name a single object, idea, action, or quality.

> waterproof (adjective) unable to be penetrated by water; often used to describe materials or fabrics that are coated with rubber or plastic

Breaking a compound word into its base words can help you figure out its meaning. Compound words can be written as a single word, as a hyphenated word, or as two separate words.

> earthquake = earth + quake   brother-in-law = brother + in + law   square dance = square + dance

A. Identifying Compound Words

Complete the chart below by breaking each compound word into its base words. Then write the meaning of the compound word, using a dictionary if needed. Finally, complete the sentences using the correct word from the chart.

Compound word	Base words	Meaning
self-defense		
wildcat		
ice skate		
jack-o'-lantern		
sideways		

1. Carving a face into a pumpkin makes it a _____.

2. Dominic likes to ski and _____ in the winter.

3. I am taking a class in _____ so I can learn to protect myself.

4. Andrea took a step _____ to avoid the mud puddle.

5. The Canada lynx is a type of _____.

Lesson 29 # Compound Words   *More Practice*

B. Compound Words in Action

For each word below, add one or more words to form a compound word. Then
write a sentence using each compound word correctly. Use a dictionary if you
need to check whether the compound word you use is spelled as one word, as
more than one word, or with a hyphen.

1. over_____ _____

2. _____ball _____

3. fire_____ _____

4. grand_____ _____

5. head_____ _____

6. _____house _____

7. _____tail _____

8. tooth_____ _____

9. heart_____ _____

10. _____time _____

C. Vocabulary Challenge

Circle the ten compound words in the following paragraphs. Then write their
meanings on the lines.

Recently I had a heart-to-heart talk with my grandmother. She said that if I
showed more self-control and did some chores at dinnertime, she would
help me buy the skateboard I have wanted for so long.

"You have to promise to ride it only in the driveway and on the sidewalk," she
explained. "And don't bump into any passersby!"

If I spend a little less on fast food, I should have enough money by
Thanksgiving Day.

1. _____   6. _____

2. _____   7. _____

3. _____   8. _____

4. _____   9. _____

5. _____   10. _____

Homonyms

Words that are spelled and pronounced the same but have different meanings are called **homonyms.** Homonyms are listed in the dictionary in separate numbered entries. Each entry may have multiple meanings. The dictionary entry for two homonyms of *bluff,* for example, is shown below:

bluff[1] *verb* **1.** to mislead or deceive, especially by using a false display of confidence or strength *noun* **2.** the act of intimidating by a false display of confidence or strength

bluff[2] *noun* a steep riverbank or cliff

She could **bluff** many people with her bold talk, but I knew that she was afraid. (meaning 1.1)

The deer stared down at us from the grass-covered **bluff.** (meaning 2)

A. Identifying Homonyms

Circle the homonyms in each pair of sentences. Then write a brief definition of each word. Use a dictionary if needed.

1. The sailor stood at the bow of the ship. _____

   All the actors took a bow when the play was over. _____

2. Please put those apples in a bowl. _____

   Would you rather bowl or play checkers? _____

3. Let me introduce you to the party's host. _____

   She will be serving a host of appetizers for us to enjoy. _____

4. In general, I lean toward vegetarian meals. _____

   I eat lean pieces of meat sometimes. _____

5. Is there enough milk in the pitcher? _____

   The team's star pitcher has a sore arm. _____

6. How do you spell your name? _____

   Would you like to sit down for a spell? _____

7. The toddler decided to run away and hide. _____

   The rug was made from animal hide. _____

8. Those tools belong in the shed. _____

   Do all snakes shed their skin? _____

9. If you drive off now, you will strand me. _____

   You should brush that strand of hair off your sweater. _____

10. Those heavy boots will hamper your running speed. _____

    Is all the picnic food in the hamper? _____

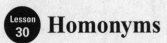

Homonyms

More Practice

B. Homonyms in Action

For each item, choose the homonym from the list that makes sense in both
sentences and write it in the blanks. Use a dictionary if needed.

1. herd / head / fair / right

   My cookie recipe won first prize at the county
   _____.

   I don't think it's _____ that I have
   to stay home tonight.

2. fawn / pore / stand / order

   I wish you wouldn't _____ over
   her. Nobody believes your flattery!

   The slender _____ stayed close
   to its mother.

3. polished / slapped / smash / ground

   Eleanor _____ the coffee beans
   before breakfast.

   The _____ was muddy after
   the storm.

4. stem / down / pit / away

   Get _____ from there this instant!

   The pillow is stuffed with goose
   _____.

5. awful / base / mean / average

   How can you be so _____
   and cruel?

   What do you _____ by that
   remark?

6. tale / deck / story / account

   That's quite a _____ she told us.

   Dr. Fell's office is on the second
   _____ of this building.

C. Vocabulary Challenge

Read the definitions given and identify each pair of homonyms. Then use each in
a sentence. Use a dictionary if needed.

1. a large, black bird / the sound a rooster makes

   homonyms: _____ / _____

   sentence 1: _____

   sentence 2: _____

2. not stale / impudent, disobedient, sassy

   homonyms: _____ / _____

   sentence 1: _____

   sentence 2: _____

3. a formal dance / a round object

   homonyms: _____ / _____

   sentence 1: _____

   sentence 2: _____

Lesson 31

Homophones and Easily Confused Words

Teaching

Many sets of English words sound the same but have different spellings and meanings. These sets of words are called **homophones,** from the Greek words *homos,* meaning "same," and *phonos,* meaning "sound."

Word	Pronunciation	Meaning
brake	brāk (rhymes with *fake*)	to slow or stop
break	brāk (rhymes with *fake*)	to smash or otherwise divide in pieces

Homophones can lead to spelling mistakes. You may mean, "I was careful not to break the dish," but if you write "I was careful not to brake the dish," you have made a spelling error. Here are other examples of homophones.

coarse (rough), course (path or school subject)

flew (past tense of *fly*), flu (a sickness also called influenza)

forth (forward), fourth (between third and fifth)

hoarse (rough-sounding), horse (an animal)

instance (example), instants (brief periods)

know (be familiar with), no (negative)

pail (bucket), pale (light-colored)

cent (one penny), scent (smell), sent (past tense of send)

heal (cure, make well), heel (the back part of the foot), he'll (he will)

right (correct or opposite of left), rite (ceremony), write (put words on paper)

A. Identifying Homophones

Circle the homophones in each sentence. Then write a brief definition of each word. Use a dictionary if needed.

1. It's about time that the cat got its food and water._____

2. When I asked him to put the box on its side, he sighed wearily. _____

3. When the weather became chilly, Fred decided to make a bowl of chili._____

4. There was peace in our house after we ate a piece of pie. _____

5. My favorite flower is the rose, so I intend to plant rows of them._____

6. The sea was calm and beautiful for as far as the eye could see. _____

7. The long hall seems an endless way to haul bags of groceries._____

8. After the bolt of lightning, the sky began lightening. _____

9. Have you read the blue book or the red one?_____

10. The bird could soar despite its sore wing. _____

Homophones and Easily Confused Words

More Practice

B. Homophones in Action

| maze / maize | peak / peek | heed / he'd | raze / raise | wurst / worst |
| stationary / stationery | pale / pail | weed / we'd | cellar / seller | reel / real |

Answer each riddle using a pair of homophones from the list above. You may have to switch the order of the words. Use a dictionary if needed.

1. What do you call a bucket that is a light color? _____

2. What do you call a look at a mountaintop? _____

3. What is another way of saying "He would pay attention"? _____

4. What do you call a person who exchanges basements for money? _____

5. What do you call a network of paths that go through a cornfield? _____

6. How would you say, "Put that up, then tear it down"? _____

7. What do you call a genuine spool? _____

8. What do you call writing paper that does not move? _____

9. How would you say, "We would tear those unwanted plants out of the ground"? _____

10. What do you call the most terrible sausage? _____

C. Vocabulary Challenge

The following paragraph includes twelve misspelled homophones. Read the passage and circle the incorrect words. Then write the correct words on the lines. Use a dictionary if needed.

Hour school's knew principle is very strict. He past by us in the hallway won day and gave us detention for being noisy. I no its important for rules too bee enforced. Still, theirs know reason to overdue it.

_____   _____   _____

_____   _____   _____

_____   _____   _____

_____   _____   _____

Lesson 32 # Homographs

Teaching

Many sets of English words are spelled the same but have different pronunciations and meanings. These sets of words are called **homographs,** from the Greek words *homos,* meaning "same," and *graphos,* meaning "written." They are often listed in separate numbered entries in the dictionary.

> When Regina had pneumonia, she was an **invalid** for a month.
> Rashid's driver's license became **invalid** when it expired.

Homograph	Pronunciation	Part of Speech	Meaning
invalid[1]	ĭn′ və-lĭd	noun	a sick, injured, or disabled person; often used to describe a person who has been sick for a long time
invalid[2]	ĭn-văl′ ĭd	adjective	not valid or proper; without force or foundation

A. Identifying Homographs

Read aloud each pair of sentences. Circle the correct phonetic respelling of each bold-faced homograph. Use the pronunciation key below to help you. You may also use a dictionary if needed.

1. (clŏs, clōs, clōz) Please **close** the door.

   (clŏs, clōs, clōz) That was a **close** call.

2. (dĕz′ ərt, dĭ-zûrt′, dēz-zhûrt′) The Sahara is a very large **desert.**

   (dûz′ ərt, dĭ-zûr′t, dēz-zhûrt′) The soldier decided to **desert** before the battle.

3. (kŏns-ōōl′, kən-sōl′, kŏn′ sōl′) The TV is inside a walnut **console.**

   (kŏns-ōōl′, kən-sōl′, kŏn′ sōl′) I tried to **console** Colin when his pet died.

4. (ĕn-trăns′, ĕnt′-rānz, ĕn′ trəns) Fireworks displays **entrance** many people.

   (ĕn-trăns′, ĕnt′-rānz, ĕn′ trəns) The **entrance** to the park featured flowering shrubs.

5. (mĭn′ ĭt, mī-nōōt′, mī′-nōōt) That bug is so **minute** that I can hardly see it.

   (mĭn′ ĭt, mī-nōōt, mī′-nōōt) I can't wait one more **minute** for my birthday.

6. (ĭn′ sĕns′, īns-ĕnz′, ĭn-sĕns′) The parking ticket seemed to **incense** Mr. Kandor.

   (ĭn′ sĕns′, īns-ĕnz′, ĭn-sĕns′) My sister burns **incense** while she does her yoga routine.

7. (ăk′ sēz, ăk sēz′, ăk′ sĭz) Tom carefully drew the X and Y **axes** onto graph paper.

   (ăk′ sēz, ăk sēz′, ăk′ sĭz) Lorna always sharpens two **axes** before she begins cutting firewood.

8. (kən-vûrs′, kŏn′ vûrs, kən′ vûrz) Reba heard her parents **converse** quietly in the next room.

   (kən-vûrs′, kŏn′ vûrs, kən′ vûrz) No matter what I tell my little brother to do, he does the **converse**.

9. (pē′ kĭd, pĕkd, pēkt) The wind gusted around the **peaked** roof.

   (pē′ kĭd, pĕkd, pēkt) Felix has been looking **peaked** and tired lately.

10. (kŏn′ tĕnt, kōn′ tĕnt, kən-tĕnt′) Jing-mei was perfectly **content** just watching the ocean.

    (kŏn′ tĕnt, kōn′ tĕnt, kən-tĕnt′) There are some errors in the **content** of that book.

Pronunciation Guide

ă p**a**t; oi b**oy**; ô p**aw**; th **th**in; ā p**ay;** ĭ p**i**t; ou **ou**t; th **th**is; är c**are;** ī p**ie;** ŏŏ t**oo**k; hw **wh**ich; ä f**a**ther; îr p**ier;** ōō b**oo**t; zh vi**s**ion; ĕ p**e**t; ŏ p**o**t; ŭ c**u**t; ə **a**bout, it**e**m; ē b**e;** ō t**oe;** ür **ur**ge; ♦ regionalism
Stress marks: ′ (primary); ′ (secondary), as in **dictionary** (dĭk′ shə-nĕr′ē)

Lesson 32 | Homographs

More Practice

B. Homographs in Action

Read aloud the passage below. Circle the correct phonetic respelling of each bold-faced homograph. Write a brief definition of each homograph. Use the pronunciation key from the previous page and context clues to help you. You may also use a dictionary if needed.

Janis plays **lead** guitar and sings vocals in a band called Don't Look Now. Her friend Nate plays **bass.** Their drummer is Eric. Nate's uncle, Mr. Coates, works for a **record** company. When he heard the band perform **live** at a picnic last summer, he was impressed. He didn't even care that Nate almost knocked over the **buffet** table while taking a **bow.** "Let's get you into the recording studio," he said to the band. "Will your parents **object** if I make you into stars?" Fortunately, all the band members' parents were **present** at the picnic. The only one who was tempted to **refuse** was Janis's mother. "I don't want my daughter to **wind** up burned out and exhausted before she's 20," she said. Janis promised to set her sights on long-term career goals.

1. (lēd, lĕd) meaning: _____

2. (băs, bās) meaning: _____

3. (rĭ-kôrd′, rĕk′ ərd) meaning: _____

4. (līv, lĭv) meaning: _____

5. (bə-fā′, bŭf′ ĭt) meaning: _____

6. (bō, bŏu) meaning: _____

7. (ŏb-jĕkt′, ŏb′ jĭkt) meaning: _____

8. (prĕz′ ənt, prĭ-zĕntĕ) meaning: _____

9. (rĕf′ yōōs, rĭ-fyōōz′) meaning: _____

10. (wīnd, wĭnd) meaning: _____

C. Vocabulary Challenge

Choose a homograph from the word bank below to complete each sentence. Then write a word that rhymes with the homograph. Use a dictionary if needed.

do   tear   sow   dove   wound

1. Albert _____ his wristwatch.

   Rhyming word: _____

2. A gray _____ on the windowsill stared at me.

   Rhyming word: _____

3. The singer did voice exercises, starting with "_____, re, mi."

   Rhyming word: _____

4. The first seeds I _____ every spring are sweet peas.

   Rhyming word: _____

5. I didn't think you could _____ such thick fabric.

   Rhyming word: _____

Lesson 33 # Analogies

Teaching

Like similes and metaphors, **analogies** are comparisons. In literature, an analogy is expressed using figurative language. In an analogy problem, the analogy is expressed using two groups of words. The relationship between the first pair of words is the same as the relationship between the second pair of words. An analogy problem can be stated either using symbols or as a sentence.

Athlete is to *team* as *actor* is to *cast.*

(First group set in capital letters) (Second group set in small letters)

ATHLETE : TEAM :: actor : cast

(Means "is to") (Means "as")

Here are some relationships that are often expressed in analogies.

Relationship	Example
Part to whole (A is part of B)	ATHLETE : TEAM
Synonym (A means the same as B)	HONEST : VIRTUOUS
Antonym (A is the opposite of B)	FRIEND : ENEMY
Item to category (A is an example of B)	POODLE : DOG
Worker to tool (A works with B)	FARMER : PLOW
Grammar (A is grammatically related to B)	RUN : RAN
Degree of intensity (A is less or more intense than B)	WARM : HOT

A. Identifying Analogies

beverage	brush	remember	agile	lender
flower	invite	noisy	penicillin	outrageous

Write the word from the list above that best completes each analogy. Then write the relationship expressed in the analogy. Use the chart to help you. You may also use a dictionary if needed.

1. PLUMBER : WRENCH :: painter : _____

   relationship: _____

2. FEAR : TERROR :: _____ : loud

   relationship: _____

3. BRITTLE : FRAGILE :: graceful : _____

   relationship: _____

4. UNKNOWN : FAMOUS :: _____ : borrower

   relationship: _____

5. BAD : TERRIBLE :: odd : _____

   relationship: _____

6. MEASLES: DISEASE :: _____ : medicine

   relationship: _____

7. VOLUME : ENCYCLOPEDIA :: stem : _____

   relationship: _____

8. COMPETE : COMPETITION :: _____ : invitation

   relationship: _____

9. BASKETBALL : SPORT :: tea : _____

   relationship: _____

10. RELUCTANT : EAGER :: _____ : forget

    relationship: _____

Analogies

More Practice

B. Analogies in Action

Circle the word in parentheses that best completes each analogy. Then write the type of relationship the analogy expresses. Use the chart on the previous page to help you. You may also use a dictionary if needed.

EXAMPLE STUDY : CRAM :: (eat, eaten, fast) : *devour*
relationship: degree of intensity

1. FINGER : HAND :: spoke : (bolt, wheel, metal)

   relationship: _____

2. SHY : BASHFUL :: (quiet, loud, furious) : soft-spoken

   relationship: _____

3. AGILE : (AGILITY, LIVELY, CLUMSY) :: bright : dim

   relationship: _____

4. (SCIENTIST, ASTRONOMY, TELESCOPE) : SCIENCE :: snake : reptile

   relationship: _____

5. NICE-LOOKING : GORGEOUS :: (acceptable, flawless, faulty) : perfect

   relationship: _____

6. WRITER : (PENCIL, WRITTEN, AUTHOR) :: carpenter : hammer

   relationship: _____

7. IDOL : IDOLIZE :: drama : (dramatize, play, dramatic)

   relationship: _____

8. SHRINK : (SHRUNK, EXPAND, REDUCE) :: destroy : ruin

   relationship: _____

9. (TEACHER, PARENT, SCHOOL) : FACULTY :: dial : clock

   relationship: _____

10. FIREFIGHTER : HOSE :: gardener : (garden, shovel, worker)

    relationship: _____

C. Analogies in Literature Challenge

Read each passage below and identify the analogy, or comparison, in it.

1. Walter looked at the papers piled high on his desk and spilling over onto the floor. He could hardly walk into his room without hearing the crunch of wrinkled pages underfoot. He felt like one of those birds that makes its nest by weaving together chewed scraps of paper.

   Analogy: _____

2. The day Jan buried his dog, the sky cried with him.

   Analogy: _____

3. Sandra was sitting in the backyard avoiding the party. She jumped when she heard a noise, but it was just a little gray kitten. He looked even more scared of her than she was of him. He paused and then walked toward her slowly. He looked ready to run, but when she held out her hand he sniffed it. Sandra petted him, took a deep breath, and went back to the party.

   Analogy: _____

Using Your Strategies

Lesson 34

You have learned several basic strategies for figuring out a word's meaning:

> using the dictionary
>
> using context clues (general, restatement, definition, comparison, contrast, example)
>
> analyzing word parts (bases, roots, affixes)
>
> considering the meaning of related words.

Using a dictionary to learn the meaning of a new word is a good strategy for building your vocabulary. However, looking up a word means interrupting your reading. The other three strategies—using context clues, analyzing word parts, and learning from related words—can help you predict the meanings of new words *while* you read. You can look up the definitions later if you still need help.

A. Vocabulary Strategies in Action: Fiction

Read the following paragraph. Figure out what the underlined words mean using the strategies listed above. Then fill in the answers and circle the strategy or strategies you used.

I was looking for a part-time job. When I saw the job advertisement posted on the school bulletin board, I was hopeful. The ad read:

> Student Help Wanted!
>
> The main office needs after-school help with <u>collating</u> (assembling in the correct order) the Student Handbook. If you are a reliable and <u>conscientious</u> worker, we need your energy!

I submitted an application the next day. A few days later, the teacher in charge of the Student Handbook asked to interview me. During the interview the teacher showed me how much work still needed to be done before the handbooks could be <u>disseminated</u> to all the students. The deadline for the project, she explained, had been <u>postponed</u> several times due to <u>inexcusable</u> delays. I told her I was still interested in the job. She was pleased and I got the job.

1. collating   meaning: _____
   strategy: context   word parts   related word   dictionary

2. conscientious meaning: _____
   strategy: context   word parts   related word   dictionary

3. disseminated meaning: _____
   strategy: context   word parts   related word   dictionary

4. postponed   meaning: _____
   strategy: context   word parts   related word   dictionary

5. inexcusable   meaning: _____
   strategy: context   word parts   related word   dictionary

Lesson 34

Using Your Strategies

More Practice

B. Using Vocabulary Strategies

Read the following paragraph. Write the meaning of the underlined words using the strategies listed above. Then fill in the strategy or strategies you used.

No one knows the role of dancing as a form of self-expression in <u>prehistory</u>. <u>Archaeologists</u> think it might have developed as early as speech and language. They base their ideas on what is known about the <u>ritual</u> dances practiced by <u>hunter-gatherers</u> societies that have survived into modern times.

Now one archaeologist has established what he says is an <u>illustrated</u> record of dancing from 9,000 to 5,000 years ago. The pictures are collected from pottery and carved stone found in the Middle East. Several of the painted figures show people in a line or with linked hands. There is some <u>resemblance</u> to current folk dancing or even a Broadway chorus line.

1. prehistory   meaning: _____

   strategy:_____

2. Archaeologists   meaning: _____

   strategy:_____

3. ritual   meaning: _____

   strategy:_____

4. hunter-gatherers   meaning: _____

   strategy:_____

5. illustrated   meaning: _____

   strategy:_____

6. resemblance   meaning: _____

   strategy:_____

C. Using Vocabulary Strategies

Write a paragraph using the words listed below. Apply the vocabulary strategies you have learned when you create your sentences so that a classmate would have to use these strategies to understand the four words.

affectionate   embarrassment   crimson   apology

Name _____ Date _____

Personal Word List

Use the space below and on the next pages to create a list of words you want to learn. Write the definition for each word and use it in a sentence to make sure you make the word your own.

_____

_____

_____

_____

_____

_____

_____

_____

_____

_____

_____

_____

_____

_____

_____

_____

_____

_____

_____

_____

_____

Personal Word List (continued)

Personal Word List (continued)

_____

_____

_____

_____

_____

_____

_____

_____

_____

_____

_____

_____

_____

_____

_____

_____

_____

_____

_____

_____

_____

_____

Personal Word List (continued)

_____

_____

_____

_____

_____

_____

_____

_____

_____

_____

_____

_____

_____

_____

_____

_____

_____

_____

_____

_____

Academic Vocabulary

Contents

Academic Vocabulary Lessons

Academic Words—History

Academic Vocabulary

feudalism *n.* a political system in Europe and Japan between the 9th and 15th centuries in which tenants, or vassals, worked the land for their lord. [Old English: root *feoh,* cattle, or property, and the suffixes *-al,* relating to, and *-ism,* practice of.]

manor *n.* a large piece of land held by a lord and worked by his tenants, or vassals; estate.

market *n.* a place where people meet to buy and sell goods; *v.* to trade goods.

medieval *adj.* relating to the Middle Ages, from about 500 to 1500.

merchant *n.* a person who buys and sells goods.

vassal *n.* the tenant on a feudal manor who owed his loyalty to the lord and was protected by him; tenant.

Break It Down—feudalism

	root	suffix	suffix
word part	**feoh**		**ism**
meaning		relating to	

A. Match each word with its definition. Write the letter of the matching word in the blank.

_____ 1. a buyer and seller of goods   A. feudalism

_____ 2. the tenant or slave   B. manor

_____ 3. a large estate   C. market

_____ 4. a place where goods are bought and sold   D. medieval

_____ 5. a political system in Europe and Japan   E. merchant

_____ 6. relating to the Middle Ages   F. vassal

B. Write the letter of the word or phrase that best completes each sentence.

_____ 1. You would expect a **vassal** to be
    a) a hard worker.
    b) lazy.
    c) rich.

_____ 2. In a **market** you might find
    a) food.
    b) clothing.
    c) all of the above.

_____ 3. **Feudalism**
    a) still exists today.
    b) was a political system in the Middle Ages.
    c) dealt with manufacturing machinery.

_____ 4. You would expect a **merchant** to
    a) care about money and trade.
    b) love art and music.
    c) own a farm.

_____ 5. On a **manor** you probably would not see
    a) vassals working in the fields.
    b) a lord supervising the vassals.
    c) a steel mill.

_____ 6. The **medieval** era
    a) was a time when most people were evil.
    b) was also known as the Middle Ages.
    c) ended two hundred years ago.

Academic Words—History

Academic Vocabulary

classical *adj.* relating to the ideas, art, literature (writings), and architecture (building design) of the ancient Greeks and Romans.

Enlightenment *n.* a movement of the 18th century that valued critical examination of traditional beliefs. [Greek: prefix *en-*, in, the root *leukos,* white, and the suffixes *-en,* cause to be, and *-ment,* process of.]

humanism *n.* a devotion to human values and arts.

patron *n.* a wealthy supporter of an artist or writer.

rationalism *n.* a belief in the power of human reason as a way to gain knowledge.

Renaissance *n.* rebirth, or revival, in classical arts and sciences that began in 14th-century Italy. [Latin: prefix *re-,* again, root *nasci,* to be born, and the suffix *-ance,* process of.]

Break It Down—enlightenment

prefix	root	suffix	suffix
word part →	→	> **en** →	> **ment**
meaning ▶ in	white	cause to be	

A. Write the letter of the vocabulary word that best completes each sentence.

_____ 1. A devotion to human values and arts is known as
    a) humanism.
    b) rationalism.
    c) the Renaissance.

_____ 2. A wealthy supporter of an artist or writer is called
    a) rationalism.
    b) the Enlightenment.
    c) a patron.

_____ 3. A rebirth of interest in classical learning that began in 14th-century Italy is
    a) rationalism.
    b) humanism.
    c) the Renaissance.

_____ 4. A belief in the power of human reason as way to gain knowledge is called
    a) rationalism.
    b) humanism.
    c) the Renaissance.

_____ 5. Ideas and achievements that relate to ancient Greece and Rome are referred to as
    a) a patron.
    b) the Renaissance.
    c) classical.

_____ 6. The 18th-century movement that valued reason over traditional values is called
    a) humanism.
    b) the Enlightenment.
    c) the Renaissance.

B. Fill in each blank in the paragraph with the correct vocabulary word.

    classical   Enlightenment   patron   rationalism   Renaissance

In 14th-century Italy, the _____ brought the world out of the Middle Ages.

With _____ Greek and Roman ideas as inspiration, artists flourished,

especially if they had a _____ to support them. In the 18th century, a new

movement, the _____, arose. Based on a belief in _____ or the

power of reason, this movement helped shape modern thought.

Lesson 3 — Academic Words—History

Academic Vocabulary

clergy *n.* the officials of a church.

divine *adj.* being or having the nature of a god.

dogma *n.* a belief or system of beliefs said to be true by a figure of authority or institution.

expulsion *n.* the act of forcing out. [Latin: prefix *ex-*, out, the root *pellere*, to drive, and the suffix *-ion*, process.]

Inquisition *n.* actions taken by the Roman Catholic Church to suppress beliefs that were different from the teachings of the Church.

monastery *n.* a place where people who have taken religious vows live and work.

persecution *n.* the harassment of people who differ in race, religion, or social class. [Latin: prefix *per*, through, and root *sequi*, to follow, and the suffix *-tion*, process of.]

theology *n.* the study of religions.

Break It Down—persecution

prefix	root	suffix
per	**sequi**	
		process of

word part ▶
meaning ▶

A. Match each word with its definition. Write the letter of the matching word in the blank.

_____ 1. having the nature of a god

_____ 2. the study of religions

_____ 3. a system of beliefs said to be true by an authority

_____ 4. harassment of people of different race or religion

_____ 5. the act of forcing out

_____ 6. the home of people who have taken religious vows

_____ 7. the officials of a church

_____ 8. actions taken to suppress beliefs that were different from the teachings of the Roman Catholic Church

A. clergy
B. divine
C. dogma
D. expulsion
E. Inquisition
F. monastery
G. persecution
H. theology

B. Write **T** if the sentence is true and **F** if it is false.

_____ 1. People in a **monastery** do scientific experiments.

_____ 2. The act of **expulsion** is like throwing someone out the door.

_____ 3. **Persecution** is a way of showing people that you accept who they are.

_____ 4. If you are interested in the relationship between organisms and their environment, study **theology.**

_____ 5. The **Inquisition** was an organized way of answering people's questions about God.

_____ 6. Someone who is too good to be true might be said to be almost **divine.**

_____ 7. Someone in the **clergy** would be good person to talk to about religion.

_____ 8. If you go against **dogma,** you may be punished.

Academic Words—History

after *adv.* following; behind.

before *adv.* earlier; ahead.

consequence *n.* effect; result. [Latin: prefix *con-*, with, and root *sequi,* to follow, and the suffix *-ence,* condition of.]

during *adv.* while.

inside *n., adj., adv.* internal; inner; within.

outside *n., adj, adv.* external; outer.

Break It Down—consequence

prefix	root	suffix
word part	**sequi**	
meaning with		condition of

A. Match each word with its synonym. Write the letter of the matching word in the blank.

_____ 1. while

_____ 2. within

_____ 3. result

_____ 4. earlier

_____ 5. outer

_____ 6. following

A. after

B. before

C. consequence

D. during

E. inside

F. outside

B. Write the letter of the word or phrase that best completes each sentence.

_____ 1. If feudalism was a political system that existed **during** the Middle Ages, then
a) feudalism and the Middle Ages occurred at the same time.
b) feudalism happened 100 years before the Middle Ages.
c) feudalism was outside the Middle Ages.

_____ 2. If persecution was a **consequence** of the Inquisition, then
a) the Inquisition happened 50 years after persecution.
b) persecution happened outside the Inquisition.
c) the Inquisition was a cause of widespread persecution.

_____ 3. If you put the lord **inside** the castle, then the castle
a) is a consequence of the lord.
b) is outside the lord.
c) was originally inside the lord.

_____ 4. If the merchant is **outside** the market, he must
a) not be inside the market.
b) be the same as the market.
c) be a consequence of the market.

_____ 5. Which pair of words are *not* opposites?
a) inside/outside   b) before/after   c) during/consequence

_____ 6. The word that is most similar to *consequence* is
a) outside.   b) during.   c) result.

Academic Words—Math

Academic Vocabulary

absolute value *n.* the numerical value of a number. *The absolute value of –9 is 9.*

coefficient *n.* a number or symbol multiplied by an unknown quantity in an algebraic expression. *The coefficient is 15 in the expression 15x - 6.* [Latin: prefix *co-*, with, the root *efficere*, to make happen, and the suffix *-ient*, causing.]

exponent *n.* a number written to the right and above a number or symbol indicating the number of times that number is multiplied by itself. *The exponent in 4^3 is 3, and it means 4x4x4.* [Latin: prefix *ex-*, outside, and root *ponere*, to place, and the suffix *-ent*, condition of.]

function *n.* a mathematical statement that indicates how two variables are related. *The equation 2x2+7x=y is a function.*

rational numbers *n.* numbers that can be expressed as integers (whole numbers) or numbers that can be divided by each other. *Zero is not a rational number; but 1, 57, $^2/_3$ are rational numbers.*

root *n.* a quantity multiplied by itself a given number of times. *The third root of 8 is 2, and it would be expressed as $2^3 = 8$, or 2 x 2 x 2 = 8.*

Break It Down—exponent

word part	prefix	root	suffix
word		ponere	ent
meaning	outside		

A. Match each word with its example. Write the letter of the matching word in the blank.

____1. 7 in 7 and -7

____2. $y = x + 6$

____3. 50 in 50x

____4. 2 in x^2

____5. $8^2 = 64$

____6. 8, 97, $^1/_2$

A. absolute value

B. coefficient

C. exponent

D. function

E. rational numbers

F. root

B. Write **T** if the sentence is true and **F** if it is false.

____1. The **absolute value** of a number is its sign.

____2. A statement that shows how two variables are related is a **function.**

____3. Zero is a **rational number.**

____4. In the expression $7x^3 + 13x + 4$, 7 and 13 are **coefficients.**

____5. In the expression $2x^3 + 4x + 8$, 4 is an **exponent.**

____6. The **root** of x^3 is x.

Lesson 2 Academic Words—Math

binomial *n.* an algebraic expression with two terms. *The expression a + bx is a binomial expression.* [Latin: prefix *bi-,* two, and root *nomin,* name, and the suffix *-ial,* characterized by.]

bisector *n.* a straight line that cuts a line or an angle in half.

diagonal *n.* a line that joins two vertices of a rectangle that are not next to each other.

polynomial *n.* an algebraic expression with one or more terms consisting of a constant multiplied by a variable. *The expression a + bx² + cx³ is a polynomial expression.*

similar *adj.* having the same shape.

slope *n.* the slant of a line.

Break It Down–binomial

prefix	root	suffix
word part ➤	➤ **nomin** ➤	➤
meaning ➤ two		characterized by

A. Write the letter of the vocabulary word that best completes each sentence.

_____ 1. Triangles that have the same shape but a difference size are
a) binomial.
b) similar.
c) diagonal.

_____ 2. The expression $3x^2 + 14x - 5$ is an example of
a) a slope.
b) a bisector.
c) a polynomial.

_____ 3. The slant of a line is its
a) slope.
b) similar.
c) bisector.

_____ 4. A line that divides an angle in half is called
a) a slope.
b) a binomial.
c) a bisector.

_____ 5. A line that connects two vertices of a rectangle that are not next to each other is
a) a diagonal.
b) a polynomial.
c) similar.

_____ 6. The expression $x^5 + x$ is
a) a bisector.
b) a binomial.
c) a slope.

B. Fill in each blank in the paragraph with the correct vocabulary word.

binomial   bisector   diagonal   polynomial   similar   slope

Algebra consists of constants, variables, and coefficients. Algebraic expressions may

have only two terms, a _____, or many terms, a _____. In

geometry, you can actually cut a line or an angle in half with a _____,

connect opposite corners of a rectangle with a _____, calculate the

_____, or slant, of a line, and learn to recognize figures that are

_____, or have the same shape.

Lesson 7 Academic Words—Math

altitude *n.* the length of a perpendicular line segment (forming a right angle to the base) from the vertex, or top, of a triangle to its opposite side.

hypotenuse *n.* the side of a right-angled triangle that is opposite the right angle; the slanted side of the triangle. [Greek: prefix *hypo-,* under, and root *teinousa,* stretching.]

line segment *n.* the part of a line between two points on the line.

midpoint *n.* the center of a line segment.

ray *n.* a straight line extending from a point.

sector *n.* the part of the circle bounded by two radii (the line segments that extend from the center of the circle to its circumference) and the included arc.

Break It Down—hypotenuse

	prefix	root
word part		teinousa
meaning	under	

A. Write the letter of the word or phrase that best completes each sentence.

____ 1. A **line segment**
    a) extends forever.
    b) does not have a midpoint.
    c) is part of a line.

____ 2. The **midpoint** of a line
    a) is a ray.
    b) is opposite a right angle.
    c) is the point at the middle of the line.

____ 3. A **hypotenuse** is part of
    a) a triangle.
    b) a circle.
    c) a sector.

____ 4. A **sector** is bounded by
    a) a hypotenuse.
    b) an arc and two radii.
    c) a midpoint.

____ 5. The **altitude** of a triangle is
    a) its hypotenuse.
    b) a sector.
    c) a perpendicular line segment.

____ 6. A **ray** is a kind of
    a) sector.
    b) line.
    c) triangle.

B. Write **T** if the sentence is true and **F** if it is false.

____ 1. A **line segment** can have a midpoint.

____ 2. The **altitude** of a right triangle is a sector.

____ 3. The **hypotenuse** is the slanted side of a right triangle.

____ 4. A **ray** is the arc of a circle.

____ 5. A **sector** does not include any line segments, or radii.

____ 6. The line segment does not have a **midpoint.**

Academic Words—Math

Academic Vocabulary

around *adv.* extending along all sides. *The circumference of a circle goes around the entire circle; the perimeter goes around a rectangle.*

between *prep.* in the space that separates; intermediate; in the middle. [Old English: prefix *be-*, across, and root *twa*, two.]

curved *adv.* having no sharp breaks or angles.

length *n.* the longest dimension of an object.

linear *adv.* like a straight line.

width *n.* the shortest dimension of an object, measured at right angles to its length.

Break It Down—between

	prefix	root
word part		**twa**
meaning	across	

A. Match each word with its example. Write the letter of the matching word in the blank.

_____ 1. like a straight line

_____ 2. the perimeter of a rectangle

_____ 3. the longest side, or 4' in an object 4' x 3'

_____ 4. the arc of a circle

_____ 5. the shortest dimension, or 3' in an object 6' x 3'

_____ 6. the 4 in 545

A. around

B. between

C. curved

D. length

E. linear

F. width

B. Write the letter of the word or phrase that best completes each sentence.

_____ 1. **Around** a rectangle is
a) all the sides.
b) curved.
c) in between.

_____ 2. If x is **between** y and z,
a) x is around y.
b) x is the length.
c) x is in the middle of y and z.

_____ 3. If the **length** of an object is
a) its shortest dimension.
b) its longest dimension.
c) a curved object.

_____ 4. Something that is **linear**
a) is curved.
b) could be measured as a length or width.
c) is around a circle.

_____ 5. Something that is **curved**
a) has a sharp angle.
b) is broken.
c) is not linear.

_____ 6. **Curved** and **linear**
a) have the same meaning.
b) mean around and between.
c) have opposite meanings.

Lesson 9 — Academic Words—Science

Academic Vocabulary

absorb *v.* to take in. [Latin: prefix *ab-*, from, and root *sorbere*, to suck up.]

reflect *v.* to turn away from or bend back, *Light will reflect off a mirror.* [Latin: prefix *re-*, back, and root *flectere*, to turn.]

refract *v.* to deflect from straight path; to change the course on entering a different material. [Latin: prefix *re-*, back, and root *frangere*, to break.]

retina *n.* the part of the eye that is sensitive to light and sends images to the brain.

spectrum *n.* the display of colors formed when a beam of light is refracted from a prism, arranged in order of wavelength.

wavelength *n.* the distance from one point of a wave of light to the same point on the next wave.

Break It Down—absorb

word part	prefix	root
		sorbere
meaning	from	

A. Match each word with its definition. Write the letter of the matching word in the blank.

_____ 1. the part of the eye that is sensitive to light

_____ 2. to turn away or bend back

_____ 3. to take in

_____ 4. the array of colors of light produced by a prism

_____ 5. to deflect; to change direction when entering a different material

_____ 6. the distance from one point of a wave of light to the same point on the next wave

A. absorb

B. reflect

C. refract

D. retina

E. spectrum

F. wavelength

B. Fill in each blank in the paragraph with the correct vocabulary word.

absorb   reflect   refract   retina   spectrum   wavelength

Light is made up of waves. The color of the light depends on the length of its

waves, or _____. If a ray of light passes through a glass prism, the

waves change course, or _____, and break into the colors of the

_____. Something looks red to us, for example, because its materials

turn back, or _____, red light and take in, or _____, light

of other colors. When we see a red apple, the image is sent from the light-

sensitive _____ of the eye to our brain.

Academic Words—Science

Academic Vocabulary

chromosome *n.* the part of a cell that carries the genes, or DNA, for creating a new generation.

DNA *n.* the molecule that makes up genes and carries the information passed on from parent to child.

dominant *adj.* A trait, such as brown eyes, that appears if a child receives the gene from just one parent.

gene *n.* a unit on a chromosome that carries information about a particular characteristic, or trait.

mitosis *n.* the division of a cell into two exact copies of itself. [Greek: root *mitos,* thread, and the suffix *-is,* process.]

recessive *adj.* a trait, such as blue eyes, that appears only if a child receives the gene from both parents.

Break It Down—mitosis

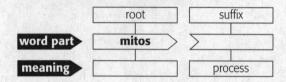

A. Write the letter of the word or phrase that best completes each sentence.

____ 1. A **gene**
    a) contains many chromosomes.
    b) carries information in the form of DNA.
    c) is the result of mitosis.

____ 2. A **recessive** trait
    a) is very common.
    b) the only type of trait.
    c) appears in a child only if both parents passed on the trait.

____ 3. **DNA**
    a) passes on information from parent to child.
    b) is outside the chromosome.
    c) is not part of a cell.

____ 4. If a person has a **dominant** trait,
    a) both parents must have passed it on.
    b) the person is very strong.
    c) at least one parent passed it on.

____ 5. You would find a **chromosome**
    a) in DNA.
    b) in a cell.
    c) in a dominant trait.

____ 6. After **mitosis** occurs in a cell
    a) the cell dies.
    b) the new cell contains half of the original cell.
    c) there are two cells exactly like the original cell.

B. Write **T** if a sentence is true and **F** if it is false.

____ 1. **DNA** plays a part in what organisms look like.

____ 2. **Chromosomes** contain genes.

____ 3. People have both **recessive traits** and **dominant traits.**

____ 4. **Mitosis** is a way that dominant cells destroy recessive cells.

____ 5. A **gene** carries information about a particular trait.

____ 6. An example of a **dominant trait** is blue eyes.

Lesson 11 # Academic Words—Science

Academic Vocabulary

asexual *n.* a type of reproduction that does not involve the union of cells from two individuals. *Cell division, or budding, is an example of asexual reproduction.*

cell *n.* the smallest unit of living matter that can exist by itself; the basis of all life.

chloroplast *n.* the part of a plant cell that contains the green coloring chlorophyll; where water and sunlight are changed into sugars. [Greek; root *chloro,* greenish yellow, and suffix *-plast,* molded, or cell.]

circulation *n.* the flow of materials through a vessel. *The movement of blood through the body is an example of circulation.*

mitochondria *n.* the parts of the cell outside the nucleus that produce energy for the cell (singular, mitochondrion).

nucleus *n.* the central part of a cell that contains the cell's hereditary material and controls its growth and reproduction.

Break It Down—chloroplast

root	suffix
word part **chloro** >	>
meaning	cell

A. Write the letter of the word or phrase that best completes each sentence.

____ 1. The central part of a cell that controls its growth and reproduction is its
    a) mitochondria.
    b) nucleus.
    c) chloroplast.

____ 2. The part of a plant cell where water and sunlight are changed into sugar is
    a) the mitochondria.
    b) the nucleus.
    c) the chloroplast.

____ 3. The smallest unit of life that can exist on its own is
    a) a cell.
    b) a chloroplast.
    c) the mitochondria.

____ 4. Reproduction that does not involve two individuals
    a) is asexual.
    b) is impossible.
    c) takes place in the mitochondria.

____ 5. The flow of blood through the body
    a) takes place through asexual reproduction.
    b) starts in the nucleus.
    c) is an example of circulation.

____ 6. The parts of the cell outside the nucleus that produce its energy
    a) is circulation.
    b) are the mitochondria.
    c) is asexual.

B. Fill in each blank in the paragraph with the correct vocabulary word.

    asexual   cell   chloroplast   mitochondria   nucleus

The _____ is the basis of all life. It includes a central _____

and, outside that, energy-producing _____. In plants, you'll also find

_____, which gives the plant its green color and produces starch and

energy. This unit of life is also where reproduction begins. Reproduction can occur by two

individuals uniting, or in an _____ process, such as cell division or budding.

Academic Words—Science

Academic Vocabulary

develop *v.* to grow or unfold.

part *n.* a portion, element, or unit of something larger.

size *n.* amount or extent, as weight or volume.

transmit *n.* to send or pass *Parents transmit genetic information to their children.* [Greek: prefix *trans-,* across, and root *mittere,* to send.]

whole *n.* a complete thing, often with parts that work together as one; *adj.* complete.

within *adv.* inside.

Break It Down—transmit

prefix	root
word part →	> **mittere**
meaning → across	

A. Match each word with its definition. Write the letter of the matching word in the blank.

_____ 1. inside   A. develop

_____ 2. send   B. part

_____ 3. grow   C. size

_____ 4. portion   D. transmit

_____ 5. amount   E. whole

_____ 6. complete   F. within

B. Write **T** if the sentence is true and **F** if it is false.

_____ 1. A **whole** is smaller than its largest part.

_____ 2. Living things usually increase in size as they **develop.**

_____ 3. Children **transmit** genetic information to their parents.

_____ 4. A nucleus and mitochondria are **within** a cell.

_____ 5. A **part** makes up the whole.

_____ 6. Your weight is a measure of your **size.**

Spelling

Contents

Lesson 1 # Silent *e* words and suffixes   *Teaching*

us**e** + age	= usage	believ**e** + able	= believable	refus**e** + al	= refusal
creat**e** + ive	= creative	televis**e** + ion	= television	literat**e** + ure	= literature
continu**e** + ous	= continuous	confus**e** + ion	= confusion	secur**e** + ity	= security
insur**e** + ance	= insurance	stor**e** + age	= storage	valu**e** + able	= valuable
surviv**e** + al	= survival	narrat**e** + ive	= narrative	complet**e** + ion	= completion
pleas**e** + ure	= pleasure	ridicul**e** + ous	= ridiculous	revis**e** + ion	= revision
matur**e** + ity	= maturity	ignor**e** + ance	= ignorance		

Lesson Generalization: A **suffix** is a word ending that changes the use of a word. When you add a suffix that begins with a vowel to a word that ends with a silent **e,** drop the **e.**

A. Complete the following exercise.

1. In the first row, what suffix has been added to base words to form spelling words? _____

   Write the words. _____   _____

2. In the second row, what suffix has been added to base words to form spelling words? _____

   Write the words. _____   _____

3. In the third row, what suffix has been added to base words to form spelling words? _____

   Write the words. _____   _____

4. In the fourth row, what suffix has been added to base words to form spelling words? _____

   Write the words. _____   _____

5. In the fifth row, what suffix has been added to base words to form spelling words? _____

   Write the words. _____   _____

6. In the sixth row, what suffix has been added to base words to form spelling words? _____

   Write the words. _____   _____

7. In the seventh row, what suffix has been added to base words to form spelling words? _____

   Write the words. _____   _____

8. In the eighth row, what suffix has been added to base words to form spelling words? _____

   Write the words. _____   _____

9. In the ninth and tenth rows, what suffix has been added to base words to form spelling words?

   _____   Write the words. _____   _____

   _____   _____

B. On a separate sheet of paper, use each of the spelling words in an original sentence. Underline the spelling word in each sentence.

Lesson 1 Final silent *e* words and suffixes

More Practice

1. usage	6. pleasure	11. storage	16. literature
2. creative	7. maturity	12. narrative	17. security
3. continuous	8. believable	13. ridiculous	18. valuable
4. insurance	9. television	14. ignorance	19. completion
5. survival	10. confusion	15. refusal	20. revision

A. Write the spelling word that matches each clue and fill in the boxes.

1. a corrected written work

2. disorder

3. delight

4. the condition of full development

5. lack of knowledge

6. story

7. going on without a break

8. foolish

9. easy to believe

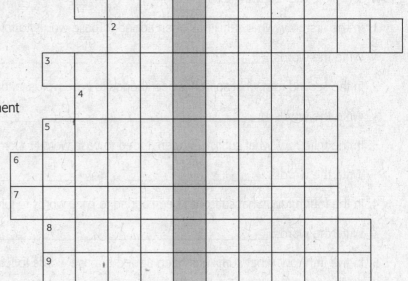

10. What spelling word is in the shaded boxes? _____

B. Write a paragraph that uses at least 15 words from the spelling list, including all of the words that are not used in exercise A.

Lesson 2

More silent *e* words and suffixes

Teaching

sincere	sincerely	hope	hoping	place	placement
secure	securely	care	careful	measure	measurement
active	activity	forgive	forgivable	involve	involving
separate	separately	like	likeness	amaze	amazing
name	naming	move	movable	advance	advancing
close	closely	require	requirement	improve	improving
waste	wasting	settle	settling		

Lesson Generalization: When you add a suffix beginning with a vowel to a word ending in silent **e,** drop the **e.** When you add a suffix beginning with a consonant to a word ending in silent **e,** keep the **e.**

A. Write the base form of each word. Then add the **ing** suffix to the base form.

Base Form   ing Form

1. involvement _____   _____

2. improvement _____   _____

3. namely _____   _____

4. settlement _____   _____

5. advancement _____   _____

6. amazement _____   _____

7. measurement _____   _____

8. forgivable _____   _____

B. Write the **–ed** form of the following words from the spelling list. Use the rule presented in the Lesson Generalization to help you determine the correct spelling.

1. separately _____

2. closely _____

3. hoping _____

4. likeness _____

5. securely _____

6. naming _____

7. wasting _____

8. requirement _____

9. placement _____

10. involving _____

11. careful _____

12. movable _____

13. settling _____

14. measurement _____

Lesson 2

Final silent *e* words and more suffixes

More Practice

1. sincerely
2. securely
3. activity
4. separately
5. naming
6. closely
7. wasting
8. hoping
9. careful
10. forgivable
11. likeness
12. movable
13. requirement
14. settling
15. placement
16. measurement
17. involving
18. amazing
19. advancing
20. improving

A. Unscramble each group of words to make a complete sentence. Be sure to use correct capitalization and punctuation. Circle the spelling words in each sentence.

1. two was amazing the between likeness the cousins.

_____

2. food forgivable good is never wasting.

_____

3. the careful was dancer to practice every placement foot .

_____

4. all securely the objects sailor fastened movable.

_____

5. pleased the sincerely is coach improving by Lyle's work.

_____

B. Find and circle 14 words from the spelling list in the following puzzle. Hint: All words are written horizontally or vertically, either forward or backward.

M	S	I	N	C	E	R	E	L	Y	K	B
E	E	N	A	F	C	L	O	S	E	L	Y
A	L	V	M	O	V	A	B	L	E	B	L
S	X	O	I	G	N	I	T	S	A	W	E
U	Y	L	N	T	W	K	A	M	P	Z	T
R	L	V	G	N	I	C	N	A	V	D	A
E	E	I	Q	V	P	L	I	M	H	C	R
M	R	N	U	R	N	D	W	A	P	H	A
E	U	G	N	I	P	O	H	Z	K	M	P
N	C	I	M	P	R	O	V	I	N	G	E
T	E	S	S	R	Z	T	H	N	J	I	S
I	S	E	T	T	L	I	N	G	A	X	W

Lesson 3 Words ending in *ate/ion*

vacate	+ ion	= vacation	locate	+ ion	= location
educate	+ ion	= education	punctuate	+ ion	= punctuation
celebrate	+ ion	= celebration	graduate	+ ion	= graduation
hesitate	+ ion	= hesitation	migrate	+ ion	= migration
translate	+ ion	= translation	complicate	+ ion	= complication
operate	+ ion	= operation	cooperate	+ ion	= cooperation
investigate	+ ion	= investigation	eliminate	+ ion	= elimination
calculate	+ ion	= calculation	circulate	+ ion	= circulation
refrigerate	+ ion	= refrigeration	regulate	+ ion	= regulation
dictate	+ ion	= dictation	duplicate	+ ion	= duplication

Lesson Generalization: A word that tells about an action is a **verb: ate** is a verb ending. A word that names something is a **noun: ion** is a noun ending. Verbs that end with **ate** can be changed to nouns by adding the suffix **ion.** The hard **t** in **ate** becomes a soft **t** in **tion.**

A. Change each of the following verbs to a noun from the word list above. Write the words on the lines provided. Then circle the letter in each verb that you delete when you create the noun form of the word.

1. duplicate _____

2. educate _____

3. circulate _____

4. translate _____

5. celebrate _____

6. migrate _____

7. calculate _____

8. refrigerate _____

9. locate _____

10. hesitate _____

11. eliminate _____

12. vacate _____

13. regulate _____

14. operate _____

15. complicate _____

16. investigate _____

17. dictate _____

B. On a separate sheet of paper, write sentences using all of the words not used above from the word list. Use both the verb and the noun form of the words in your sentences.

Lesson 3 # Words ending in *ate/ion*   *More Practice*

1. vacation	5. translation	9. refrigeration	13. graduation	17. elimination
2. education	6. operation	10. dictation	14. migration	18. circulation
3. celebration	7. investigation	11. location	15. complication	19. regulation
4. hesitation	8. calculation	12. punctuation	16. cooperation	20. duplication

A. Complete these sentences with the **ion** forms of words from the spelling list above. Then circle the **ate** verb that appears in each sentence.

1. The detectives hoped everyone would cooperate with the _____ of the crime.

2. To eliminate the problem of overcrowding, the school's _____ ceremony is being moved to a new _____.

3. A good secretary can take _____ and correctly punctuate letters and memos.

4. The surgeon says that this _____ can regulate the heartbeat and improve blood _____.

5. I will not hesitate to try water skiing when I am on _____.

6. Are scientists able to calculate when the geese will begin their _____ from Canada?

7. Please duplicate your work on the board so the math class can see how the _____ is done.

8. If you regulate the _____ carefully, none of the food will spoil.

9. Our class is planning a special _____ for the day we graduate.

10. You must learn some new _____ when you translate written English into Spanish.

B. For each definition below, write the corresponding spelling word in both its noun and verb forms.

1. to make difficult   _____   _____

2. to keep cool   _____   _____

3. to move from   _____   _____

4. to copy   _____   _____

5. to find   _____   _____

6. to learn   _____   _____

Name _____ Date _____

Prefixes and base words

Teaching

re + double = <u>re</u>double	con + quest = <u>con</u>quest
re + commend = <u>re</u>commend	con + sequence = <u>con</u>sequence
de + serve = <u>de</u>serve	sub + urban = <u>sub</u>urban
de + part = <u>de</u>part	sub + division = <u>sub</u>division
ad + join = <u>ad</u>join	pre + diction = <u>pre</u>diction
ad + minister = <u>ad</u>minister	pre + caution = <u>pre</u>caution
ex + act = <u>ex</u>act	per + cent = <u>per</u>cent
ex + claim = <u>ex</u>claim	per + form = <u>per</u>form
in + dent = <u>in</u>dent	pro + pose = <u>pro</u>pose
in + stall = <u>in</u>stall	pro + long = <u>pro</u>long

Lesson Generalization: A prefix is a group of letters added to the beginning of a word to make a word with a different meaning. You can add a prefix directly to a base word to form a new word with a different meaning. The spelling of the base word does not change when you add a prefix.

A. Answer the following questions on the lines provided.

1. In the first column of the word list, what five prefixes have been added to base words?

_____

Write the words from the first column.

_____   _____   _____

_____   _____   _____

_____   _____

2. In the second column of the word list, what five prefixes have been added to base words?

_____

Write the words from the second column.

_____   _____   _____

_____   _____   _____

_____   _____

B. Choose eight words from the list above. Scramble the letters of each word and give them to a partner to solve. You unscramble your partner's words.

_____   _____   _____   _____

_____   _____   _____   _____

Lesson 4 # Prefixes and base words

More Practice

1. redouble	6. administer	11. conquest	16. precaution
2. recommend	7. exact	12. consequence	17. percent
3. deserve	8. exclaim	13. suburban	18. perform
4. depart	9. indent	14. subdivision	19. propose
5. adjoin	10. install	15. prediction	20. prolong

A. Complete the crossword puzzle with words from the spelling list. Each clue defines a different spelling word.

Across

1. a foretelling
2. to offer advice
3. to attach to
4. precisely correct
7. to fix in position
9. result of an action
11. an area of land divided into smaller lots
12. to double again
13. move in from the margin

Down

1. to lengthen in time
3. to manage or direct
5. a victory
6. a part of one hundred
8. located in a suburb
10. to suggest

B. On a separate sheet of paper write a paragraph that includes at least eight spelling words. Five must be those that were not used in the crossword puzzle above. Have fun with your writing—the paragraph need not be realistic.

Prefixes and roots

re + sist = re<u>sist</u>　　　　　de + tain = de<u>tain</u>

in + sist = in<u>sist</u>　　　　　con + tain = con<u>tain</u>

con + flict = con<u>flict</u>　　　pro + gress + ion = prog<u>ress</u>ion

in + flict = in<u>flict</u>　　　　re + gress + ion = reg<u>ress</u>ion

de + script + ion = de<u>script</u>ion　　de + cis + ion = de<u>cis</u>ion

in + script + ion = in<u>script</u>ion　　in + cis + ion = in<u>cis</u>ion

pre + script + ion = pre<u>script</u>ion　pre + cis + ion = pre<u>cis</u>ion

in + vent + ion = in<u>vent</u>ion　　　in + clude = in<u>clude</u>

con + vent + ion = con<u>vent</u>ion　　ex + clude = ex<u>clude</u>

pre + vent + ion = pre<u>vent</u>ion　　con + clude = con<u>clude</u>

Lesson Generalization: A root can be joined with many prefixes. Changing the prefix forms a new word. The definition of a word will provide a clue to the meaning of its root. The root **clude** means "to close."

exclude = to close out or shut out　　　include = to close in

A. Find the spelling words that begin with the following prefixes. Write the words in each group in alphabetical order.

de　　　　　　　**pre**　　　　　　　**in**

_____　_____　_____

_____　_____　_____

_____　_____　_____

re　　　　　　　**con**　　　　　　　_____

_____　_____　_____

_____　_____　_____

ex　　　　　_____　**pro**

_____　_____　_____

B. On a separate sheet of paper, write each word from the word list in an original sentence.

Prefixes and roots

More Practice

1. resist
2. insist
3. conflict
4. inflict
5. description

6. inscription
7. prescription
8. invention
9. convention
10. prevention

11. detain
12. contain
13. progression
14. regression
15. decision

16. incision
17. precision
18. include
19. exclude
20. conclude

A. Circle the thirteen hidden spelling words in the search puzzle. Words are placed forward, backwards, up or down, or diagonally.

```
I   N   C   I   S   I   O   N   N   C   N   I   I   Q   H
N   B   P   Y   C   J   M   O   V   G   F   N   K   N   L
F   I   B   R   N   O   I   G   T   T   C   S   O   C   P
L   R   N   W   E   T   N   S   R   L   P   I   J   Y   L
I   D   P   S   N   C   S   F   U   K   T   S   P   N   V
C   Z   E   E   C   C   I   D   L   P   L   T   R   L   M
T   P   V   C   P   R   E   S   I   I   Z   F   O   K   S
F   N   M   S   I   J   I   R   I   X   C   X   G   K   J
I   Q   V   B   C   S   C   P   P   O   S   T   R   V   R
L   P   X   L   L   S   I   Y   T   J   N   H   E   M   B
Y   V   Y   G   E   Z   X   O   J   I   L   N   S   R   Q
Y   Z   D   R   L   R   K   R   N   S   O   W   S   M   X
P   W   P   X   L   J   X   B   Q   N   Q   N   I   Y   N
M   N   D   R   R   E   G   R   E   S   S   I   O   N   P
G   J   Q   C   O   N   V   E   N   T   I   O   N   F   G
```

B. Expand each phrase into a sentence. Then, on your own paper, use three of the sentences in a short story that begins with the sentence: **Inspector Whodunit was baffled.**

1. the eyewitness' <u>description</u> _____

2. could only <u>conclude</u> _____

3. <u>contain</u> the missing jewels _____

4. <u>detain</u> the suspect _____

5. <u>resist</u> arrest _____

6. <u>prevention</u> of crime _____

Compound words and contractions   *Teaching*

proof + read = proofread   blue + eyed = blue-eyed
fire + proof = fireproof   one + half = one-half
time + table = timetable   ninety + four = ninety-four
life + time = lifetime   self + addressed = self-addressed
night + time = nighttime   great + aunt = great-aunt
some + one = someone   does + not = doesn't
any + time = anytime   it + is = it's
mean + while = meanwhile   there + is = there's
every + where = everywhere   here + is = here's
when + ever = whenever   would + have = would've

Lesson Generalization: When two words are connected without a change in spelling to either word, the result is called a **compound word**. A **contraction** is formed when two words are connected and an apostrophe replaces one or more omitted letters. Hyphenated words are two words joined by a hyphen.

A. What words from the list were made by forming a contraction? A compound word? A hyphen? Write the words in the correct rows below.

1. **contractions:** _____ _____

   _____ _____ _____

2. **compound words:** _____ _____

   _____ _____ _____

   _____ _____ _____

   _____ _____

3. **hyphenated words:** _____ _____

   _____ _____ _____

B. On a separate sheet of paper write each word from the list as two separate words. Then trade papers with a partner and correctly write the words as compound words, contractions, or hyphenated words.

Name _____ Date _____

Compound words and contractions

More Practice

1. proofread
2. fireproof
3. timetable
4. lifetime
5. nighttime

6. someone
7. anytime
8. meanwhile
9. everywhere
10. whenever

11. blue-eyed
12. one-half
13. ninety-four
14. self-addressed
15. great-aunt

16. doesn't
17. it's
18. there's
19. here's
20. would've

A. Write the spelling word that matches each clue and fits in the boxes.

1. as long as someone lives

2. at whatever time

3. not just anyone

4. non-flammable

5. at any moment

6. at the same time

7. after sunset

8. bus or train schedule

9. look for writing errors

10. What other spelling word
do you see in the shaded boxes?

_____

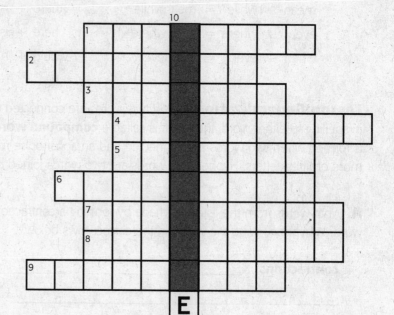

B. On your own paper, write a sentence using each set of spelling words. You may use the words in any order.

1. there's, timetable, ninety-four

2. would've, lifetime, great-aunt

3. it's, whenever, self-addressed

4. doesn't, everywhere, blue-eyed

5. here's, proofread, one-half

Lesson 7 **Silent letters**

si**gn**	**wh**ose
resi**gn**	**wh**ole
rei**gn**	an**sw**er
forei**gn**	**sw**ord
knives	**wr**itten
knocked	**wr**apped
cru**mb**s	ras**pb**erry
li**mb**s	cu**pb**oard
pa**lm**	sta**lk**
a**lm**ond	fo**lk**lore

Lesson Generalization: A **silent letter** is a letter that is not pronounced. A word's spelling may include a consonant pair in which one consonant is silent.

gn **kn** m**b** **lm** **wh** s**w** **wr** **pb** **lk**

A. Which words from the list contain the following silent partner pairs? Write the words on the lines provided.

1. **gn**

_____

_____

_____

_____

2. **kn**

_____

_____

3. **mb**

_____

_____

4. **lk**

_____

_____

5. **wr**

_____

_____

6. **lm**

_____

_____

7. **wh**

_____

_____

8. **sw**

_____

_____

9. **pb**

_____

_____

B. Choose ten words from the spelling list. On a separate sheet of paper scramble the letters of each word and then give them to a partner to write correctly. Check your placement of the silent letter in each word.

Lesson 7

Silent letters

More Practice

1. sign	6. knocked	11. whose	16. wrapped
2. resign	7. crumbs	12. whole	17. raspberry
3. reign	8. limbs	13. answer	18. cupboard
4. foreign	9. palm	14. sword	19. stalk
5. knives	10. almond	15. written	20. folklore

A. Circle the nineteen hidden spelling words in the word search puzzle. Words are written forward, backward, diagonally, and up and down.

W	R	A	P	P	E	D	S	C	S	D	S	N	P	P
R	H	F	K	S	Y	T	H	I	R	D	E	G	A	Q
A	V	O	O	P	A	K	Y	O	G	T	V	I	L	K
S	G	H	L	L	Z	D	W	D	T	N	I	E	M	Z
P	W	S	K	E	N	S	E	I	T	R	N	R	C	D
B	L	J	V	O	L	K	R	R	H	R	K	O	R	F
E	N	H	M	P	C	W	N	C	E	M	B	F	U	G
R	Z	L	X	O	X	Y	C	W	M	I	B	W	M	P
R	A	G	N	K	S	Q	S	U	W	S	G	L	B	S
Y	R	K	R	J	D	N	T	L	P	Z	X	N	S	B
K	E	X	C	M	A	J	M	F	I	B	W	G	P	J
Q	S	K	X	S	T	B	C	X	S	M	O	B	K	P
Q	I	V	X	Z	L	T	N	L	T	Z	B	A	Y	T
B	G	K	L	V	V	S	N	H	Q	R	J	S	R	C
S	N	G	J	H	Q	K	D	W	F	B	C	H	J	D

B. Which letter is silent in each combination listed below? Write your answers on the lines. Then, for each letter pair, choose one word from the spelling list that includes those letters, and use that word in a sentence on a separate sheet of paper.

1. gn _____

2. lm _____

3. wr _____

4. kn _____

5. wh _____

6. pb _____

7. mb _____

8. sw _____

9. lk _____

Review

1. pleasure	11. celebration	21. decision
2. refusal	12. cooperation	22. insist
3. usage	13. punctuation	23. nighttime
4. continuous	14. refrigeration	24. ninety-four
5. believable	15. precaution	25. doesn't
6. sincerity	16. percent	26. proofread
7. separately	17. recommend	27. foreign
8. hoping	18. consequence	28. knives
9. measurement	19. prescription	29. whose
10. improving	20. prevention	30. written

A. Complete these sentences with words from the spelling list.

1. I must _____ that everyone follow this safety _____.

2. Jane's stubborn _____ to cooperate spoiled our plans for the big _____.

3. After taking Dr. Clark's _____, Leon's health was _____.

4. A burglar alarm with a loud, _____ siren aids in crime _____.

5. Remember to _____ all of your _____ work for errors in spelling, _____, and word _____.

6. Margie's _____ to study a _____ language is a wise one.

7. Fifty _____ of the food supplies spoiled as a _____ of poor _____.

8. Jess's obvious _____ when he apologized made me believe that we could be good friends again.

B. On a separate sheet of paper use the words from the spelling list that were not used in exercise A in original sentences.

Review

A. An analogy is a special way of showing how words are related to each other. Complete each analogy with a spelling word that makes the second pair of words go together in the same way as the first pair of words.

1. **clear** is to **clarity** as **sincere** is to _____

2. **double** is to **redouble** as **commend** is to _____

3. **value** is to **believe** as **valuable** is to _____

4. **half** is to **halves** as **knife** is to _____

5. **sixty** is to **ninety** as **sixty-four** is to _____

6. **vent** is to **prevent** as **caution** is to _____

7. **usage** is to **use** as **percentage** is to _____

8. **close** is to **closely** as **separate** is to _____

9. **useful** is to **using** as **hopeful** is to _____

10. **educate** is to **education** as **refrigerate** is to _____

11. **life** is to **lifetime** as **night** is to _____

12. **bite** is to **bitten** as **write** is to _____

13. **hope** is to **hoping** as **improve** is to _____

14. **precise** is to **precision** as **decide** is to _____

B. Improve this paragraph. Circle each misspelled word and write it correctly on a separate sheet of paper. Then replace each underlined phrase with a spelling word. You may add, subtract , or change word endings.

It was getting late, and we still hadn't completed preparations for that night's victory celebrashun. If everyone <u>worked together and helped each other</u>, I knew we could finish by <u>the time it got dark</u>. Mike recomended that we separate into teams. Sean and Suzanne started refrigerating the drinks, while Greta and Paul put knifes and forks on the buffet table. As a <u>way to make sure that nothing happened</u>, Jorge steadied the ladder for pat while she hung the banners. Finally, we taped up the signs we had writen, and hoped we had not forgotten anything. It was a <u>really nice feeling</u> to stand back and see how much the appearance of the room was <u>changed for the better</u> by all of our work.

Lesson 9 **Final *y* words and suffixes**   *Teaching*

holidays	sprayed	reply	y to i + ed	= replied
highways	delayed	copy	y to i + ed	= copied
valleys	surveyed	multiply	y to i + ed	= multiplied
essays	displayed	balcony	y to i + es	= balconies
journeys	enjoying	cavity	y to i + es	= cavities
	steadying	apology	y to i + es	= apologies
		society	y to i + es	= societies
		empty	y to i + es	= empties
		county	y to i + es	= counties

Lesson Generalization: A **suffix** is an ending added to a word that changes how the word is used. If the letter before a final **y** is a vowel, do not change the **y** when you add a suffix. If the letter before a final **y** is a consonant, change the **y** to **i** before you add any suffix except **ing.** The **y** never changes before **ing.**

A. Each group of letters below is contained in a spelling word. Find the word in the spelling list, and write its **s, ed,** and **ing** forms. The last nine words will have only the **s** forms.

	s	ed	ing
1. joy	_____	_____	_____
2. tip	_____	_____	_____
3. eye	_____	_____	_____
4. play	_____	_____	_____
5. ply	_____	_____	_____
6. ray	_____	_____	_____
7. lay	_____	_____	_____

	s		s		s
8. say	_____	11. our	_____	14. cop	_____
9. log	_____	12. on	_____	15. all	_____
10. way	_____	13. day	_____	16. it	_____

B. On a separate sheet of paper use each spelling word in an original sentence.

Final *y* words and suffixes

Lesson 9

More Practice

1. sprayed	6. holidays	11. replied	16. balconies
2. displaying	7. highways	12. copied	17. societies
3. enjoying	8. valleys	13. steadying	18. cavities
4. surveyed	9. essays	14. emptying	19. apologies
5. delayed	10. journeys	15. multiplied	20. counties

A. Write the plural form of the 11 spelling words that fit in the puzzle.

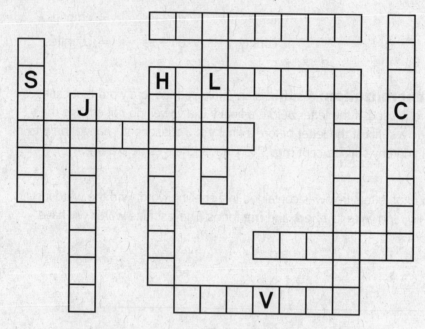

B. Write the words from the spelling list in alphabetical order. As a regular practice, if there is a word you do not know, look it up in a dictionary.

1. _____
2. _____
3. _____
4. _____
5. _____
6. _____
7. _____
8. _____
9. _____
10. _____

11. _____
12. _____
13. _____
14. _____
15. _____
16. _____
17. _____
18. _____
19. _____
20. _____

Lesson 10

Words ending in *ly/ally*

emotional	+ ly	= emotionally		music	+ ally	= musically
traditional	+ ly	= traditionally		romantic	+ ally	= romantically
national	+ ly	= nationally		academic	+ ally	= academically
accidental	+ ly	= accidentally		athletic	+ ally	= athletically
incidental	+ ly	= incidentally		frantic	+ ally	= frantically
temperamental	+ ly	= temperamentally		drastic	+ ally	= drastically
sentimental	+ ly	= sentimentally		sarcastic	+ ally	= sarcastically
historic	+ ally	= historically		specific	+ ally	= specifically
optimistic	+ ally	= optimistically		dramatic	+ ally	= dramatically
periodic	+ ally	= periodically		automatic	+ ally	= automatically

Lesson Generalization: An adjective is a word that modifies a noun. An adverb modifies a verb, an adjective or another adverb. Add **ly** to adjectives to form adverbs.

Add the ending **ally** to words that end with the letters **ic** to form adverbs.

A.

1. All of the words before the plus sign are adjectives. The words after the equal sign are adverbs.

   What suffix is added to adjectives ending in **al** to make them adverbs? _____

   Write those adverbs.

   _____   _____   _____   _____

   _____   _____   _____

2. What suffix is added to adjectives ending in **ic** to make them adverbs? _____

   Write those adverbs.

   _____   _____   _____

   _____   _____   _____

   _____   _____   _____

   _____

B. Use at least eight of the adverbs in the word list to write a letter to your friend about your latest escapade. You are a person who tends to be a bit dramatic in your descriptions. You have even been known to exaggerate.

Words ending in *ly/ally*

Teaching

1. emotionally	6. temperamentally	11. musically	16. drastically
2. traditionally	7. sentimentally	12. romantically	17. sarcastically
3. nationally	8. historically	13. academically	18. specifically
4. accidentally	9. optimistically	14. athletically	19. dramatically
5. incidentally	10. periodically	15. frantically	20. automatically

A. Unscramble these syllables to make spelling words.

1. ly cal si mu _____
2. to ly au mat cal i _____
3. mo al e ly tion _____
4. dem ly ac i cal a _____
5. ti sen ly tal men _____
6. cal mis op ly ti ti _____
7. al di tion ly tra _____
8. ti ly cal dras _____
9. mat dra ly i cal _____
10. ly tal den ci ac _____

11. od ri pe ly i cal _____
12. cal let ly ath i _____
13. i cif cal spe ly _____
14. den in tal ly ci _____
15. ti ly fran cal _____
16. cal i tor ly his _____
17. ly sar cal cas ti _____
18. per tal tem ly a men _____
19. ly na al tion _____
20. man cal ro ly ti _____

B. Write the spelling word that is a synonym (a word that has almost the same meaning) for the underlined word.

1. John <u>unintentionally</u> brought the wrong book to class. _____
2. These sliding doors open <u>mechanically</u>. _____
3. The President visits our state <u>regularly</u>. _____
4. The camper looked <u>desperately</u> for water to douse the fire. _____
5. The actor behaved <u>moodily</u> when he didn't get his way. _____
6. This map shows <u>exactly</u> which route to take. _____
7. This town <u>customarily</u> has a parade on the Fourth of July. _____
8. The coach spoke <u>hopefully</u> about her team's future. _____
9. The baseball scout was looking for <u>physically</u> talented players. _____
10. The drought will <u>severely</u> reduce our water supply. _____

Lesson 11

The suffixes *ance/ant* and *ence/ent*

Teaching

attend + ance	=	attend<u>ance</u>		anci<u>ent</u>
avoid + ance	=	avoid<u>ance</u>		sci<u>ence</u>
annoy + ance	=	annoy<u>ance</u>		consci<u>ence</u>
apply + ance	=	appli<u>ance</u>		effici<u>ent</u>
defy + ance	=	defi<u>ance</u>		suffici<u>ent</u>
guide + ance	=	guid<u>ance</u>		frequ<u>ent</u>
defend + ant	=	defend<u>ant</u>		sequ<u>ence</u>
contest + ant	=	contest<u>ant</u>		delinqu<u>ent</u>
inhabit + ant	=	inhabit<u>ant</u>		adoles<u>cent</u>
descend + ant	=	descend<u>ant</u>		cres<u>cent</u>

Lesson Generalization: The suffixes **ance** and **ant** are commonly added to complete words. The suffixes **ence** and **ent** are commonly added to roots. They are used after the letters **ci, qu,** and **sc.**

A.

1. Notice that the suffixes in the first column are added to complete words. What are those suffixes?

_____   _____

Write the spelling words that are made by joining a complete word with its suffix.

_____   _____   _____

_____   _____   _____

_____   _____   _____

_____

2. What suffixes are added to the roots in the second column?

_____   _____

Write the spelling words that are made by joining a root and its suffix.

_____   _____   _____

_____   _____   _____

_____   _____   _____

B. On a separate sheet of paper write the spelling words and a brief definition for each.

Lesson 11 The suffixes *ance/ant* and *ence/ent*

More Practice

Tested List

1. attendance	6. guidance	11. ancient	16. frequent
2. avoidance	7. defendant	12. science	17. sequence
3. annoyance	8. contestant	13. conscience	18. delinquent
4. appliance	9. inhabitant	14. efficient	19. adolescent
5. defiance	10. descendant	15. sufficient	20. crescent

A. Rewrite each incomplete word with the correct ending.

1. defend

_____

2. annoy

_____

3. contest

_____

4. attend

_____

5. suffici

_____

6. guid

_____

7. delinqu

_____

8. avoid

_____

9. inhabit

_____

10. effici

_____

11. cresc

_____

12. consci

_____

13. anci

_____

14. appli

_____

15. sequ

_____

16. adolesc

_____

17. defi

_____

18. sci

_____

19. frequ

_____

20. descend

_____

B. Write the spelling word that is related in some way to each group of words.

1. stove, refrigerator, vacuum cleaner _____

2. teen-ager, youth, juvenile _____

3. native, resident, citizen _____

4. biology, chemistry, physics _____

5. heir, grandson, great-granddaughter _____

6. first, second, third _____

7. competition, judge, winner _____

8. pest, bother, irritation _____

9. lawyer, judge, jury _____

10. modern, antique, futuristic _____

Prepositional prefixes

Teaching

supernatural	precede	transcontinental
supersonic	premeditated	transfusion
superlative	forewarned	transplant
superintendent	forecast	transmission

subordinate	postpone
subterranean	postwar
submerge	postscript
subconscious	postdated

Lesson Generalization: A **preposition** is a word that is placed *before* a noun or pronoun to show the relationship between that word and another word in the sentence. The noun or pronoun following the preposition is called the **object** of the preposition. Prefixes often have the meaning of prepositions.

pre (before) + **position** = **preposition**.

A. Each word below means the same as one or more of the prefixes from your list. In alphabetical order under each word, write the spelling words that contain that prefix.

under (sub)   **before (pre)**   **above (super)**

_____   _____   _____

_____   _____   _____

_____   _____   _____

_____   _____   _____

across (trans)   **after (post)**

_____   _____

_____   _____

_____   _____

_____   _____

B. On a seperate sheet of paper, scramble the prefixes and base words from the word list and then put a different prefix with each base. Trade papers with a partner and match up the prefixes with their correct bases.

Prepositional prefixes

More Practice

1. supernatural	6. subterranean	11. forewarned	16. postdated
2. supersonic	7. submerge	12. forecast	17. transcontinental
3. superlative	8. subconscious	13. postpone	18. transfusion
4. superintendent	9. precede	14. postwar	19. transplant
5. subordinate	10. premeditated	15. postscript	20. transmission

A. Write the spelling word that matches each definition. Then circle the word in the definition that gives the meaning of the prefix.

1. below consciousness

_____

2. note after a letter

_____

3. to predict beforehand

_____

4. person who oversees a job

_____

5. to go before

_____

6. a transferring of something across

_____

7. under the earth

_____

8. the sending of a message across

_____

9. beyond the speed of sound

_____

10. after a war

_____

11. to put under water

_____

12. planned or schemed beforehand

_____

13. dated after the present

_____

14. below another in rank

_____

15. above all others in quality

_____

16. beyond the laws of nature

_____

17. to dig up and move to another place

_____

18. across a continent

_____

19. to put off until later or after

_____

20. warned beforehand

_____

B. Using a dictionary, find additional words that use the five prefixes. Write one word for each prefix on a separate sheet of paper and then compare your list with others in the class.

Lesson 13 # The assimilated prefix *ad*

dis + count	= discount		re + cent	= recent
ad + count	= account		ad + cent	= accent
in + fection	= infection		in + fluence	= influence
ad + fection	= affection		ad + fluence	= affluence
re + peal	= repeal		dis + proved	= disproved
ad + peal	= appeal		ad + proved	= approved
re + semble	= resemble		re + sistance	= resistance
ad + semble	= assemble		ad + sistance	= assistance
re + tract	= retract		in + tention	= intention
ad + tract	= attract		ad + tention	= attention

Lesson Generalization: Assimilated means to be made a part of. When the last letter of a prefix changes to match the first letter of a root, the prefix is said to be assimilated. The prefix **ad** is assimilated more often than any other prefix. It also causes more double-consonant spelling problems than any other prefix.

ad + similat + ed = assimilated   (to) (same or similar) (made similar to)

A.

1. Ten words in the spelling list begin with the prefix ad. The base words change their spelling when the prefix ad is added. Write these ten spelling words.

_____   _____   _____   _____

_____   _____   _____   _____

_____   _____

2. The ten other words from the list do not change their spelling when their prefix is added. Write these prefixes and the words from the list that begin with each.

Prefix   **Words**

_____   _____   _____

_____   _____   _____   _____

_____   _____   _____   _____

_____   _____

B. On a separate sheet of paper write the spelling words in alphabetical order and write a short definition for each.

Lesson 13

The assimilated prefix *ad*

More Practice

1. discount	5. repeal	9. retract	13. influence	17. resistance
2. account	6. appeal	10. attract	14. affluence	18. assistance
3. infection	7. resemble	11. recent	15. disproved	19. intention
4. affection	8. assemble	12. accent	16. approved	20. attention

A. Complete each sentence with two spelling words that have the same root.

1. Can you _____ the pieces of this puzzle to _____ a dog?

2. Everyone _____ of the scientist's research until his findings were

   _____.

3. The council may _____ the new law if we _____ directly
   to the mayor.

4. This coupon entitles shoppers to a _____ when they open a charge

   _____.

5. My _____ is to attract the _____ of the audience.

6. Nations with great _____ sometimes use their wealth to

   _____ other nations.

7. Her _____ visit to England may account for her slight

   _____.

8. The mother showed much _____ when treating her baby's

   _____.

9. I need your _____ in overcoming the _____ to my plan.

10. The candidate wanted to _____ his earlier statement to _____
    more voters.

B. All of the words in the spelling list begin with one of four letters: **a, r, d, i.**
Use as many spelling words as possible in four alliterative sentences. (Alliteration
is the repetition of a beginning consonant sound.) Circle the spelling words.

Detective Dawson (disproved) the department director's description of the daring (discount) deal.

1. _____

2. _____

3. _____

4. _____

Hard and soft *c/g*

cancel	circular	delicious	gorgeous	gymnastics
conceal	capacity	innocence	gigantic	religion
conceited	concentrate	gadget	argument	contagious
cynical	physician	garage	tragedy	intelligence

Lesson Generalization: When **c** and **g** have a soft sound, they will be followed by the letters **i, e,** or **y.** Suffixes that follow the soft **c** or **g** will always begin with an **i** or an **e: ian, ion, ious, ence.** When the letters **c** and **g** have a hard sound, they will be followed by **a, o,** or **u.**

A.

1. What letters follow a soft **c** or **g?** _____; _____; _____
   Write the words from the spelling list that have a soft **c** or **g.** Underline the soft **c** or **g** in each word.

   _____ _____ _____ _____

   _____ _____ _____ _____

   _____ _____ _____ _____

   _____ _____ _____ _____

   _____ _____

2. What letters follow a hard **c** or **g?** _____; _____; _____
   Write the words from the spelling list that have a hard **c** or **g.** Underline the hard **c** or **g** in each word.

   _____ _____ _____ _____

   _____ _____ _____ _____

   _____ _____ _____ _____

   _____

B. Write a paragraph using as many of the **c** words or **g** words as you can. Underline the soft **c's** and **g's** and circle the hard **c's** and **g's.**

Hard and soft *c/g*

More Practice

1. cancel	6. capacity	11. gadget	16. tragedy
2. conceal	7. concentrate	12. garage	17. gymnastics
3. conceited	8. physician	13. gorgeous	18. religion
4. cynical	9. delicious	14. gigantic	19. contagious
5. circular	10. innocence	15. argument	20. intelligence

A. Complete each word by adding the missing vowels. Then write each word.

1. tr__g__dy _____

2. c__n__c__l _____

3. c__nc__l _____

4. c__nc__ntr__t__ _____

5. g__r__g__ _____

6. c__rc__l__r _____

7. c__nc__ __ t __d _____

8. c__nc__ __l _____

9. r__l__g __ n _____

10. ph__s__c__ __n _____

11. __nt__ll__g__nc__ _____

12. __nn__c__nc__ _____

13. g__rg__ __ __ s _____

B. Unscramble the following word groups to form complete sentences. Circle each spelling word.

1. small of is the capacity the garage.

_____

2. weather forced gymnastics meet cancel bad to us the.

_____

3. gorgeous gingerbread delicious those houses also are.

_____

4. the mixer gigantic cement stirred motion a with circular.

_____

5. disease contagious could not he doctor his conceal from.

_____

6. helped lawyer's the argument the win him intelligence.

_____

7. proud was the inventor of gadget the not conceited but.

_____

Unstressed vowels

Lesson 15

Teaching

rel<u>a</u>tive	rel<u>a</u>ted	fant<u>a</u>sy	fant<u>a</u>stic
hum<u>a</u>n	hum<u>a</u>nity	comp<u>a</u>ny	comp<u>a</u>nion
ge<u>o</u>graphy	ge<u>o</u>graphical	democr<u>a</u>cy	democr<u>a</u>tic
emph<u>a</u>sis	emph<u>a</u>tic	all<u>e</u>rgy	all<u>e</u>rgic
gramm<u>a</u>r	gramm<u>a</u>tical	com<u>e</u>dy	com<u>e</u>dian
ang<u>e</u>l	ang<u>e</u>lic	rem<u>e</u>dy	rem<u>e</u>dial
par<u>e</u>nt	par<u>e</u>ntal	terr<u>i</u>fy	terr<u>i</u>fic
art<u>i</u>st	art<u>i</u>stic	host<u>i</u>le	host<u>i</u>lity
med<u>i</u>cine	med<u>i</u>cinal	mel<u>o</u>dy	mel<u>o</u>dious
bi<u>o</u>logy	bi<u>o</u>logical	edit<u>o</u>r	edit<u>o</u>rial

Lesson Generalization: Unstressed vowels cause spelling problems because they are difficult to hear and identify. Many words have a form in which the accent shifts to a different syllable. A vowel that is difficult to identify in one form may be easier to hear in the other form. A vowel in an accented syllable is pronounced more clearly. Is the **e** more clearly pronounced in **com' e dy** or **co me' di an ?**

A. Read the second word in each pair aloud. The underlined vowel is in a stressed syllable. It is easy to hear the sound of that vowel.

B. Read the first word in each pair aloud. The underlined vowel is in an unstressed vowel. These vowels are more difficult to hear and identify. To help you spell these words, think about how the vowel sounds in the other form of each word. Then write the first word of each pair correctly on the lines below.

_____ _____ _____ _____

_____ _____ _____ _____

_____ _____ _____ _____

_____ _____ _____ _____

Unstressed vowels

Lesson 15

More Practice

1. relative	6. angel	11. fantasy	16. remedy
2. human	7. parent	12. company	17. terrify
3. geography	8. artist	13. democracy	18. hostile
4. emphasis	9. medicine	14. allergy	19. melody
5. grammar	10. biology	15. comedy	20. editor

A. Use your dictionary to mark the accented syllable (´) in each word shown below.

1. gram mar	6. hu man	11. par ent	16. em pha sis
2. fan ta sy	7. com pa ny	12. com e dy	17. an gel
3. bi ol o gy	8. med i cine	13. rel a tive	18. hos tile
4. ter ri fy	9. rem e dy	14. art ist	19. al ler gy
5. mel o dy	10. de moc ra cy	15. ed i tor	20. ge og ra phy

B. Use the clues to find spelling words that fit the puzzle.

Across

1. the opposite of tragedy

4. drug used to treat diseases

5. tune

8. pertaining to the earth's surfaces

Down

1. guests

2. person who revises written work

3. winged, guardian spirit

6. showing special attention or stress

7. person skilled in the fine arts

Lesson 16 **Review**

Review

1. cavities
2. delaying
3. multiplied
4. societies
5. accidentally
6. athletically
7. historically
8. specifically

9. appliance
10. guidance
11. ancient
12. frequent
13. adolescent
14. subconscious
15. forecast
16. postpone

17. transcontinental
18. supernatural
19. resemble
20. assistance
21. recent
22. affection
23. tragedy
24. conceited

25. physician
26. contagious
27. allergy
28. medicine
29. related
30. comedian

A. Complete each analogy with a word from the spelling list.

1. **sonic** is to **supersonic** as **natural** is to _____

2. **cavities** is to **cavity** as **tragedies** is to _____

3. **access** is to **recess** as **accent** is to _____

4. **merge** is to **submerge** as **conscious** is to _____

5. **contract** is to **contracted** as **conceit** is to _____

6. **assist** is to **resist** as **assemble** is to _____

7. **apology** is to **apologies** as **society** is to _____

8. **warn** is to **forewarn** as **cast** is to _____

9. **intention** is to **attention** as **infection** is to _____

10. **creative** is to **created** as **relative** is to _____

11. **angelic** is to **angel** as **allergic** is to _____

12. **companion** is to **company** as **comedian** is to _____

13. **religion** is to **religious** as **contagion** is to _____

14. **music** is to **musically** as **athletic** is to _____

15. **active** is to **activities** as **cave** is to _____

B. On a separate sheet of paper write a sentence for each spelling word that was not included in exercise A.

Review

Lesson 16

A. Complete the sentences with spelling words.

1. This reproduction of the _____ city is _____ accurate.

2. The events for the _____ boys in this category will be _____ by
   the _____.

3. The _____ saw that Lara had taken too much of the strong
   _____.

4. The customer _____ asked for that particular kitchen _____.

5. After hearing the weather _____, we decided to _____
   our long _____ plane trip until tomorrow.

6. Her _____ causes her to have _____ sneezing attacks, which
   have _____ now that spring is here.

7. We appreciated his wise _____ and able _____.

8. Psychics and other people interested in the _____ exchanged ideas at a
   _____ convention.

B. Three words in each row follow the same spelling pattern. Write the word that
does not follow the pattern.

1. enjoyed	appliance	replies	copied	_____
2. delicious	innocence	physician	musical	_____
3. postwar	precede	disproved	supersonic	_____
4. contestant	accident	resistance	annoyance	_____
5. tragedy	apology	argument	gymnastics	_____
6. appeal	affection	attention	resemble	_____
7. recent	attract	discount	repeal	_____
8. counties	highways	essays	journeys	_____
9. guidance	medicinal	hostility	humanity	_____
10. angels	balconies	comedies	remedies	_____

Lesson 17 · *1 + 1 + 1* words and *VAC* words

plan	planning	ship	shipment	patrol	patrolled
star	starred	sad	saddest	rebel	rebellion
slip	slippery	dim	dimmer	forgot	forgotten
jog	jogging	upset	upsetting	forget	forgetting
grab	grabbed	begin	beginning	equip	equipment
stop	stopping	control	controlled	commit	commitment
swim	swimmer	regret	regrettable		

Lesson Generalization: A word that has **1** syllable, **1** vowel, and **1** final consonant is called a **1 + 1 + 1** word: set. A word that has a single vowel in a final accented syllable with one final consonant is called a **VAC** word: up set'. Double the final consonant of a **1 + 1 + 1** word or a **VAC** word before a suffix that begins with a vowel. Do not double the final consonant before a suffix that begins with a consonant.

The word pairs in the first column are **1 + 1 + 1** words. The word pairs in the second column are **VAC** words.

A.

1. Find the **1 + 1 + 1** words in the list. Write the words with their suffixes as shown in the word list.

_____ _____ _____

_____ _____ _____

_____ _____ _____

_____

2. Find the **VAC** words in the list. Write the words with their suffixes as shown in the word list.

_____ _____

_____ _____ _____

_____ _____ _____

_____

B. On a separate sheet of paper, scramble the words in the spelling list (those with suffixes). Trade lists with a partner and unscramble your partner's words.

Lesson 17

1 + 1 + 1 words and *VAC* words

More Practice

1. planning	6. stopping	11. upsetting	16. rebellion
2. starred	7. swimmer	12. beginning	17. forgotten
3. slippery	8. shipment	13. controlled	18. forgetting
4. jogging	9. saddest	14. regrettable	19. equipment
5. grabbed	10. dimmer	15. patrolled	20. commitment

A. Form spelling words by adding endings to the base words.

1. commit + ment _____   11. slip   + ery   _____

2. star   + ed   _____   12. grab   + ed   _____

3. equip   + ment _____   13. control + ed   _____

4. forgot + en   _____   14. regret + able _____

5. jog   + ing   _____   15. begin   + ing   _____

6. rebel   + ion   _____   16. upset   + ing   _____

7. patrol + ed   _____   17. stop   + ing   _____

8. dim   + er   _____   18. forget + ing   _____

9. plan   + ing   _____   19. swim   + er   _____

10. sad   + est   _____   20. ship   + ment _____

B. Circle the 16 spelling words that are hidden in this puzzle. They may be placed forward, backward, diagonally, up, or down.

```
C  O  N  T  R  O  L  L  E  D
D  I  M  M  E  R  G  B  Q  P
S  J  P  D  H  S  R  P  U  A
J  W  M  Q  M  H  A  L  I  T
S  O  I  Y  J  I  B  A  P  R
F  S  G  M  K  P  B  N  M  O
T  O  W  G  M  M  E  N  E  L
S  G  R  X  I  E  D  I  N  L
E  K  X  G  S  N  R  N  T  E
D  T  K  R  O  T  G  G  K  D
D  E  R  R  A  T  S  D  X  H
A  U  P  S  E  T  T  I  N  G
S  B  S  L  I  P  P  E  R  Y
F  B  E  G  I  N  N  I  N  G
F  O  R  G  E  T  T  I  N  G
```

Name _____ Date _____

transmit	transmitting	confer	conference	visit	visiting
omit	omitted	differ	difference	pilot	piloted
admit	admitted	suffer	suffered	enter	entered
permit	permitted	offer	offered	alter	altered
transfer	transferring	happen	happened	murmur	murmuring
refer	referred	gallop	galloping	labor	labored
prefer	preference	orbit	orbiting		

Lesson Generalization: A **VAC** word must have a final accented syllable.
Some **VAC** words have a form in which the accent shifts to a different syllable
when the suffix is added. For these forms, do **not** double the final consonant of
the base word when you add the suffix: con-fer' con'fer-ence.

A. Say each word aloud.

1. Look at the first word of each word pair. Notice that each word ends in a single vowel/single

   consonant combination. In the first eight words, which syllable is accented? _____

   Which syllable is accented in the last twelve words? _____ Write the **VAC** words.

   _____ _____ _____ _____

   _____ _____ _____ _____

2. What happens to the spelling of a **VAC** word when **ed** or **ing** is added? _____
   Write the VAC words with these suffixes.

   _____ _____ _____ _____

   _____ _____

3. Notice that some **VAC** words have a form in which the accent shifts to a different vowel when the
   suffix is added. Remember, do not double the final consonant of these base words when you add the
   suffix. What are these two words?

   _____ _____

4. What happens to the spelling of words that are not accented on the final syllable? _____
   Write these words.

   _____ _____ _____

   _____ _____ _____

   _____ _____ _____

B. On a separate sheet of paper, use the second word from each word pair in an
original sentence.

Lesson 18

Doubling final consonants

More Practice

1. transmitting	6. referred	11. offered	16. piloted
2. omitted	7. preference	12. happened	17. entered
3. admitted	8. conference	13. galloping	18. altered
4. permitted	9. difference	14. orbiting	19. murmuring
5. transferring	10. suffered	15. visiting	20. labored

A. Each spelling word is divided into two syllables. Say each word aloud and listen for the accented or stressed syllable. Mark the accented syllable. Then write the **ed** and **ing** forms of each word.

	ed	**ing**
1. con fer	_____	_____
2. en ter	_____	_____
3. suf fer	_____	_____
4. trans mit	_____	_____
5. hap pen	_____	_____
6. la bor	_____	_____
7. ad mit	_____	_____
8. dif fer	_____	_____
9. re fer	_____	_____
10. mur mur	_____	_____
11. al ter	_____	_____
12. gal lop	_____	_____
13. vis it	_____	_____
14. or bit	_____	_____
15. pre fer	_____	_____

B. On a separate sheet of paper, use each word in both its **ed** and **ing** forms in a complete sentence. Write one sentence for each form.

pilot   offer   transfer   permit   omit

The suffixes *able* and *ible*

Lesson 19

adapt + able	= adaptable		vis + ible	= visible
avail + able	= available		aud + ible	= audible
attain + able	= attainable		leg + ible	= legible
agree + able	= agreeable		ed + ible	= edible
regret + able	= regrettable		poss + ible	= possible
forget + able	= forgettable		cred + ible	= credible
control + able	= controllable		tang + ible	= tangible

adore + able	= adorable
advise + able	= advisable
excite + able	= excitable
notice + able	= noticeable
change + able	= changeable
manage + able	= manageable

Lesson Generalization: The suffix **able** means "able to be." It is commonly added to complete words to form adjectives. When **able** is added to words that end in **ce** or **ge,** the **e** must be kept to protect the soft sound of **c** or **g.**

The suffix **ible** is more commonly added to roots than to complete words. The **i** in **ible** gives the letter **g** a soft sound: **legible, tangible.**

Hint: Many words that begin with **a** use the suffix that begins with **a.**

A.

1. When **able** is added to words ending in **ce** or **ge**, the **e** must be kept to protect the soft sound of

   _____ or _____ Write the words to which this rule applies.

   _____   _____   _____

2. The suffix **able** is most often added to complete words. Write the spelling words, excluding those you wrote above, that end in **able**.

   _____   _____   _____   _____

   _____   _____   _____   _____

   _____   _____

3. The suffix **ible** is most often added to roots. Write the spelling words that end in **ible**.

   _____   _____   _____

   _____   _____   _____

B. On a separate sheet of paper, create a word search puzzle using all of the spelling words. Trade puzzles with a partner. Circle the spelling words in your partner's puzzle.

Lesson 19

The suffixes *able* and *ible*

More Practice

1. adaptable	6. forgettable	11. noticeable	16. legible
2. available	7. controllable	12. changeable	17. edible
3. attainable	8. adorable	13. manageable	18. possible
4. agreeable	9. advisable	14. visible	19. credible
5. regrettable	10. excitable	15. audible	20. tangible

A. Unscramble the letters and write the spelling words. First find and circle the **able** or **ible** endings. They are not scrambled.

1. sibleiv _____

2. cixeablet _____

3. ableroda _____

4. ptaaabled _____

5. ssibleop _____

6. vlableaia _____

7. gnatible _____

8. tablegreert _____

9. sadvablei _____

10. ibledua _____

11. ganaableme _____

12. eableearg _____

13. icenotable _____

14. deible _____

15. lableltornoc _____

16. hagablecen _____

17. dreiblec _____

18. tatableain _____

19. torfeablegt _____

20. iblegle _____

B. On a separate sheet of paper, answer each question with a complete sentence that uses an **ible** spelling word.

1. Was the handwriting in the old letter still <u>able to be read</u>?

2. Does Paul's story about his adventure seem <u>believable</u> to you?

3. Could the plant cells <u>be seen</u> without a microscope?

4. Is the leftover food still <u>fit to be eaten</u>?

5. <u>Can</u> the actor's voice <u>be heard</u> throughout the theater?

6. Did the explorers discover <u>physical</u> evidence of the lost city?

7. Is an earthquake <u>capable of happening</u> in your state?

The prefixes *com* and *in*

com + gratulate	= congratulate	in + stinct = instinct
com + tinent	= continent	in + spection = inspection
com + nection	= connection	in + numerable = innumerable
com + mon	= common	in + measurable = immeasurable
com + municate	= communicate	in + mobile = immobile
com + mand	= command	in + mature = immature
com + patible	= compatible	in + personate = impersonate
com + plicated	= complicated	in + possibility = impossibility
com + pliment	= compliment	in + pression = impression
com + bination	= combination	in + balance = imbalance

Lesson Generalization: The prefixes **com** and **in** follow the same spelling pattern. Both are spelled with an **n** before most letters of the alphabet. Both are spelled with an **m** before roots or words that begin with the letters **m**, **p**, or **b**. They are spelled this way to make more compatible combinations that are easier to pronounce.

Say **inmobile** and **immobile**. Say **comtinent** and **continent**.

Double consonants often result from joining prefixes and roots. Remember that one consonant belongs to the prefix, and one belongs to the root.

A.

1. The prefixes **com** and **in** follow the same spelling rules. Before most letters of the alphabet they are

   spelled with an _____. Write the words from the word list that follow this rule.

   _____ _____ _____ _____

   _____ _____

2. The prefixes **com** and **in** are spelled with an _____ when the root they precede begins with **m, p,** or **b.** Write the words from the list that follow this pattern.

   _____ _____ _____ _____

   _____ _____ _____ _____

   _____ _____ _____ _____

   _____ _____

B. On a separate sheet of paper, use as many of the words from the list as you can in a paragraph. Don't worry too much about the sense of the paragraph—just use the words and have fun!

Name _____ Date _____

The prefixes *com* and *in*

More Practice

1. congratulate   6. command   11. instinct   16. immature
2. continent   7. compatible   12. inspection   17. impersonate
3. connection   8. complicated 13. innumerable   18. impossibility
4. common   9. compliment   14. immeasurable   19. impression
5. communicate   10. combination 15. immobile   20. imbalance

A. Find the misspelled word in each group. Write the word correctly.

1. common
   conection
   compliment
   combination

   _____

2. impersonate
   immeasurable
   immature
   imobile

   _____

3. instinct
   innumerable
   inpression
   inspection

   _____

4. continent
   congratulate
   conpatible
   connection

   _____

5. immature
   immobile
   immeasurable
   immbalance

   _____

6. communicate
   comand
   common
   connection

   _____

B. Write the spelling word that is related to the two words on each line. One of the two words is a synonym for the spelling word. The other word is an antonym of the same spelling word. Circle the synonym. Underline the antonym.

1. simple   complex   _____

2. countless   few   _____

3. ordinary   extraordinary   _____

4. adult   childish   _____

5. order   obey   _____

6. separation   link   _____

7. movable   stationary   _____

8. agreeable   hostile   _____

9. limited   boundless   _____

10. flattery   insult   _____

Lesson 21 — More assimilated prefixes

ad + preciate	= **ap**preciate	com + respond	= **cor**respond
ad + petite	= **ap**petite	com + rection	= **cor**rection
ad + paratus	= **ap**paratus	in + rigation	= **ir**rigation
ad + parently	= **ap**parently	in + regular	= **ir**regular
ad + propriate	= **ap**propriate	in + ritate	= **ir**ritate
ad + proximately	= **ap**proximately	in + legal	= **il**legal
ad + ponent	= **op**ponent	in + lustration	= **il**lustration
ob + portunity	= **op**portunity	com + lapse	= **col**lapse
sub + ported	= **sup**ported	com + lege	= **col**lege
sub + posed	= **sup**posed	com + lection	= **col**lection

Lesson Generalization: Assimilated prefixes often result in double consonants that cause spelling problems.

The spelling of the prefixes **ad**, **ob**, and **sub** changes when they are joined to roots or base words that begin with the letter **p**:

    ad becomes **ap**   **ob** becomes **op**   **sub** becomes **sup**

The spelling of the prefixes **com** and **in** changes when they are joined to roots or base words beginning with the letter **r**:

    com becomes **cor**   **in** becomes **ir**

The spelling of the prefixes **com** and **in** changes when joined to the letter **l**:

    com becomes **col**   **in** becomes **il**

A. Correctly write each spelling word.

1. subposed _____
2. adparently _____
3. adparatus _____
4. obportunity _____
5. adpetite _____

6. inlustration _____
7. comlege _____
8. inlegal _____
9. comrection _____
10. inritate _____

B. On a separate sheet of paper use each word from the spelling list in an original sentence.

Lesson 21 # More assimilated prefixes

More Practice

1. appreciate	6. approximately	11. correspond	16. illegal
2. appetite	7. opponent	12. correction	17. illustration
3. apparatus	8. opportunity	13. irrigation	18. collapse
4. apparently	9. supported	14. irregular	19. college
5. appropriate	10. supposed	15. irritate	20. collection

A. Unscramble the syllables to make spelling words. Cross out the extra syllable or syllables in each group.

1. ri in tate ir   _____

2. posed des sup er   _____

3. de col es lapse   _____

4. i mate prox da ap ly _____

5. lec on tion col   _____

6. pre ate ci non ap   _____

7. tra in lus il tion _____

8. tite pe ap ly con   _____

9. spond dis re cor   _____

10. ty ob ni por op tu _____

11. un ly ap ent par   _____

12. lege tor oc col   _____

13. ed sup ly port   _____

14. le ni gal il   _____

15. u reg sa lar ir   _____

16. ob nent op po   _____

17. ri tion ir ga or   _____

18. tus ra pa ad ap   _____

19. pro ate up pri ap _____

20. de rec cor tion   _____

B. Find the spelling words that fit in the shapes. Then write a synonym for each word on the line.

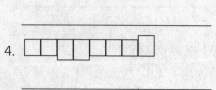

1. _____

2. _____

3. _____

4. _____

5. _____

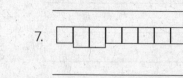

6. _____

7. _____

8. _____

9. _____

10. _____

Lesson 22 The letters *qu*

Teaching

antique	quite	aquarium
boutique	quiet	squirrel
technique	quickly	equality
	quarterly	equator
mosquito	quarrel	banquet
etiquette	quotation	ventriloquist
bouquet	quotient	
	quilted	

Lesson Generalization: The letter **q** is always followed by the letter **u** in the English language.

When **qu** is pronounced /**k**/, it can appear in the middle of a word or at the end of a word: **mosquito, antique.**

The spelling is always **que** at the end of a word.

When **qu** is pronounced /**kw**/, it can appear in the middle of a word or at the beginning of a word: **equator, quarrel.**

A. Read each word in the word list aloud. Then answer the questions.

1. Look at the underlined letters in the words. What letter combination at the end of a word makes the

   /**k**/ sound? _____ Write the words with that letter combination.

   _____ _____ _____

2. What other letter combination makes the /**k**/ sound? _____ In what part of the word

   is it found? _____ Write the words from the list with that combination.

   _____ _____ _____

3. What letter combination makes the /**kw**/ sound? _____ In what part of the word is it

   found? _____ or _____ Write the words that make the /**kw**/ sound.

   _____ _____ _____ _____

   _____ _____ _____ _____

   _____ _____ _____ _____

   _____ _____

B. On a separate sheet of paper, write several short verses that include as many of the spelling words as possible. Each verse can be on a different subject, if you wish. Make them humorous. Read your favorite to a partner.

The letters *qu*

More Practice

1. antique	6. bouquet	11. quarrel	16. squirrel
2. boutique	7. quite	12. quotation	17. equality
3. technique	8. quiet	13. quotient	18. equator
4. mosquito	9. quickly	14. quilted	19. banquet
5. etiquette	10. quarterly	15. aquarium	20. ventriloquist

A. The words in each group are related in some way. Find the spelling word that fits in each group. Write the words on the lines.

1. chipmunk, gopher, beaver _____

2. fight, argument, dispute _____

3. zoo, stable, kennel _____

4. fly, gnat, bee _____

5. divisor, dividend, remainder _____

6. shop, store, salon _____

7. feast, party, dinner _____

8. courtesy, manners, politeness _____

9. bunch, corsage, arrangement _____

10. still, silent, calm _____

11. monthly, yearly, semi-annually _____

12. method, system, style _____

B. First find the spelling word that is a synonym for the word below and place it in the shaded boxes. Then find eight more words to fit in the boxes going across.

sameness

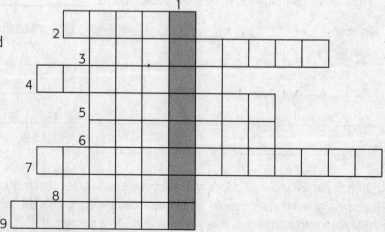

The letters *j*, *ge*, and *dge*

justice	journal	challenge	judge
juice	pajamas	language	pledge
jumbo	conjunction	damage	bridge
juvenile	rejoice	mileage	badge
jacket	injury	marriage	dodge

Lesson Generalization: The letters **j** and **g** often sound alike.

The letter **j** is used at the beginning and in the middle of words, not at the end.

Unlike the letter **g**, the letter **j** has a **soft** sound before the vowels **a, o, u.**

The letters **ge** spell the soft sound of /**j**/ at the ends of words. The letters **dge** are usually found in a one-syllable word with a short vowel.

A. Read the words in the spelling list aloud. Then answer the questions.

1. In what part of a word does the letter **j** appear?

_____

Write the words from the list that include the letter **j**. Circle the **j** in each word.

_____ _____ _____ _____

_____ _____ _____ _____

_____

2. The letter combination **ge** at the end of a word has what sound?

_____

Write the words from the list that fit this pattern. Circle the **ge** in each.

_____ _____ _____ _____

_____

3. Where are you most likely to encounter the letter combination **dge**?

_____

Write the words from the spelling list that end in **dge**. Circle the letters.

_____ _____ _____ _____

_____

B. On a separate sheet of paper, write the words from the spelling list. Circle the vowels. Say each word aloud.

The letters *j*, *ge*, and *dge*

More Practice

1. justice	5. jacket	9. rejoice	13. damage	17. pledge
2. juice	6. journal	10. injury	14. mileage	18. bridge
3. jumbo	7. pajamas	11. challenge	15. marriage	19. badge
4. juvenile	8. conjunction	12. language	16. judge	20. dodge

A. One underlined word in each phrase is part of a spelling word. The other underlined word is a clue to its meaning. Write the spelling word.

1. the right <u>age</u> for a <u>wedding</u> _____

2. no <u>award</u> for being <u>bad</u> _____

3. <u>dare</u> to give your <u>all</u> _____

4. <u>ruined</u> by <u>age</u> _____

5. <u>across</u> the <u>ridge</u> _____

6. <u>ice</u> in your <u>drink</u> _____

7. <u>jam</u> on your <u>nightshirt</u> _____

8. hid the <u>diary</u> in the <u>urn</u> _____

9. <u>joined</u> with the prefix <u>con</u> _____

10. ran a good <u>distance</u> for his <u>age</u> _____

11. <u>promised</u> to <u>edge</u> the lawn _____

12. Cleopatra's <u>youth</u> on the <u>Nile</u> _____

B. Circle the spelling words in the word search. They are placed forward, backward, up, and down. Be sure to find all twenty.

Y	S	F	K	Z	D	S	E	E	J	W	N	B	D	H	C	H
W	K	O	T	C	G	C	M	G	U	C	C	A	O	F	H	L
R	C	F	L	L	X	F	O	D	I	U	W	D	D	P	A	Z
E	J	U	S	T	I	C	E	U	C	G	Q	G	G	I	L	D
J	E	E	P	J	O	K	Z	J	E	I	B	E	E	G	L	J
O	G	G	L	C	O	N	J	U	N	C	T	I	O	N	E	O
I	D	A	E	B	S	A	M	A	J	A	P	U	C	W	N	U
C	I	M	D	I	M	I	L	E	A	G	E	V	R	K	G	R
E	R	A	G	W	E	G	Y	R	U	J	N	I	N	E	E	N
U	B	D	E	F	J	Y	A	E	L	I	N	E	V	U	J	A
E	G	A	U	G	N	A	L	M	A	R	R	I	A	G	E	L
U	R	T	E	K	C	A	J	O	B	M	U	J	G	P	W	P

Lesson 24 **Review**   *Review*

1. beginning	9. advisable	17. connection	25. equator
2. controlled	10. agreeable	18. appetite	26. justice
3. equipment	11. noticeable	19. opponent	27. judge
4. forgetting	12. changeable	20. supposed	28. marriage
5. offered	13. visible	21. illegal	29. language
6. difference	14. impossibility	22. mosquito	30. challenge
7. happened	15. communicate	23. antique	
8. referring	16. immature	24. quarrel	

A. Complete these sentences with words from the review spelling list.

1. There was only a slight weight _____ between Sean and his _____ in the wrestling match.

2. This _____ desk is _____ to be 150 years old.

3. A foolish _____ sounds the same in any _____.

4. I keep _____ to _____ with my pen pal, who lives in a country near the _____.

5. His _____ hostility made reaching an agreement an _____.

6. I think it is _____ for Lee to report what _____ to the police.

7. The superior court _____ ruled on the case.

8. The valley wasn't _____ from the summit.

9. In the _____ of the project everyone seemed _____.

10. A loss of _____ can _____ to a poor diet.

B. On a separate sheet of paper, write a paragraph or short story using as many of the spelling words as you can. Then trade papers with a partner and, without looking at the list, circle as many spelling words as you can. See who can find the most words in a partner's paper without checking the list.

Lesson 24 Review

Review

A. Complete each analogy with a word from the spelling list. Hint: These analogies are based on the forms of words.

1. **commit** is to **commitment** as **equip** is to _____

2. **bouquets** is to **bouquet** as **mosquitoes** is to _____

3. **prefer** is to **refer** as **preferring** is to _____

4. **carry** is to **carriage** as **marry** is to _____

5. **legible** is to **illegible** as **legal** is to _____

6. **complication** is to **complicate** as **communication** is to _____

7. **replaced** is to **replaceable** as **noticed** is to _____

8. **believe** is to **believable** as **advise** is to _____

9. **premature** is to **mature** as **prejudge** is to _____

10. **forgot** is to **forgetting** as **began** is to _____

11. **incredible** is to **credible** as **injustice** is to _____

12. **managed** is to **manageable** as **changed** is to _____

13. **inaudible** is to **invisible** as **audible** is to _____

14. **regrettable** is to **regretted** as **controllable** is to _____

B. Complete each analogy with a word from the spelling list. Hint: These analogies are based on relationships of ideas rather than on forms of words.

1. **new** is to **modern** as **old** is to _____

2. **adult** is to **mature** as **child** is to _____

3. **France** is to **French** as **country** is to _____

4. **drink** is to **thirst** as **food** is to _____

5. **promise** is to **pledge** as **dare** is to _____

6. **happy** is to **peace** as **mad** is to _____

7. **top** is to **north** as **center** is to _____

8. **similar** is to **likely** as **variation** is to _____

Greek combining forms

Teaching

stere	stereo	stereophonic
typós, typi	typical	stereotype
psycho	psychic	psychology
logi, logy	logical	technology
techni	technical	architect
arch	archives	archeology
patri	paternal	patriarch
genes	genesis	genealogy
hydro	hydrant	hydrophobia
phobia	phobia	acrophobia

Lesson Generalization: **Greek combining forms (GCF)** are word elements that, unlike prefixes and suffixes, can be added to either the beginning or the end of other word elements. **GCF** may be joined in the same way that the two parts of a compound word are joined. Knowing the meaning of the separate parts will help in understanding the words. The spelling of the **GCF** may change slightly when it is joined to other word parts.

The noun suffix **ant** forms the noun **hydrant** (hydro + ant).

The adjective suffix **ic** forms the adjective **psychic** (psycho + ic).

GCF joined like a compound word: patri**arch** / **arch**eology

logi is a prefix   **logy** is a suffix

A.

1. The Greek combining forms in the first column become English nouns or adjectives when suffixes are added. Write the words from the second column that are made up of a Greek combining form and a suffix. Underline the combining form in each word, and circle those words whose combining form changes spelling when the suffix is added.

_____   _____   _____

_____   _____   _____

_____

2. The words in the third column are formed by joining two Greek combining words. Write each word. Then, for each word, underline the combining form that is common to that in the first and second column. Finally, circle those words whose combining form changes spelling when joined to another combining form.

_____   _____   _____

_____   _____   _____

_____

B. On a separate sheet of paper, write the spelling words and a brief definition for each. Look up the words in your dictionary and note the meanings of the combining forms.

Greek combining forms

More Practice

1. stereo	6. psychology	11. archives	16. genealogy
2. stereophonic	7. logical	12. archeology	17. hydrant
3. typical	8. technology	13. paternal	18. hydrophobia
4. stereotype	9. technical	14. patriarch	19. phobia
5. psychic	10. architect	15. genesis	20. acrophobia

A. First look at the meaning of each of the Greek word parts listed below. Then use the meaning of the Greek parts to find spelling words that match the definitions.

phobia—fear	psycho—mind	logi, logy—reason; study of
genes—origin	hydro—water	typos, typi—type, example
stere—strong	techni—skilled	arch—first
phon—sound	patri—father	acro—highest

1. fatherly _____

2. study of origins _____

3. dealing with a skill _____

4. reasonable _____

5. "first father" or leader _____

6. fear _____

7. "first documents" or record _____

8. strong sounding _____

9. "first" skilled builder _____

10. fear of heights _____

11. fear of water _____

12. study of skill _____

13. street pipe for water _____

14. strong type _____

15. study of first people _____

16. study of the mind _____

17. concerning the mind _____

18. origin _____

19. strong-sounding record player _____

20. a usual type _____

B. Write the word from each pair of spelling words that best completes the sentence.

1. Joyce will not swim because she suffers from (hydrophobia, acrophobia). _____

2. Ralph's family has traced its (archeology, genealogy) to the sixteenth century. _____

3. A home computer is one product of modern (technology, psychology). _____

4. The discovery of fire marked the (genesis, genealogy) of a new way of life. _____

5. Consider all aspects of a problem carefully to arrive at a (logical, technical) solution. _____

6. Students of (archeology, archives) may work at actual "digs" while learning about that science. _____

7. Thomas Jefferson was the (patriarch, architect) who designed and built Monticello. _____

8. The term for any extreme fear is (phobia, acrophobia). _____

Latin combining forms

Lesson 26

quad	quarter	quadrangle
ped	pedestrian	quadruped
cent	century	centipede
grad	gradual	centigrade
annus	annual	anniversary
uni	united	universal
anima	animated	unanimous
magni	magnify	magnanimous
fac	factory	manufacture
manu	manual	manuscript

Lesson Generalization: Suffixes can be added to **Latin combining forms** to make complete words. The spelling may change slightly when other word parts are added, but the meaning will remain the same.

Two Latin combining forms may be joined like the two parts of a compound word. Unlike prefixes and suffixes, a combining form can be used in any position in a word.

A.

1. The Latin combining forms in the first column can become words when a suffix or prefix is added. The words from column two are formed by joining a combining form and a suffix or prefix. Write the words and underline the combining form in each.

   _____ _____ _____ _____

   _____ _____ _____ _____

   _____ _____

2. Combining forms of Latin words can be joined like the two parts of compound words. In what parts of a word might you find a combining form?

   _____ _____ _____

   The words from column three are created by joining combining forms. Write each word and underline its combining form from the first column.

   _____ _____ _____ _____

   _____ _____ _____ _____

   _____ _____

B. On a separate sheet of paper, create a word search puzzle using all 20 spelling words. Trade papers with a partner and solve each other's puzzles.

Latin combining forms

More Practice

1. quarter
2. quadrangle
3. pedestrian
4. quadruped
5. century

6. centipede
7. gradual
8. centigrade
9. annual
10. anniversary

11. united
12. universal
13. animated
14. unanimous
15. magnify

16. magnanimous
17. factory
18. manufacture
19. manual
20. manuscript

A. First look at the meaning of these Latin word parts. Then write the spelling word that can replace the underlined words in the phrases.

manu—hand   **magni**—large, great   **cent**—one hundred
grad—degree   **anima**—spirit   **annus**—year

1. submitted his <u>handwritten paper</u>   _____

2. a <u>hundred degree</u> thermometer   _____

3. celebrate the <u>turn of the year</u>   _____

4. caught a <u>creature with one hundred feet</u>   _____

5. <u>do or make</u> the parts <u>by hand</u>   _____

6. a <u>hand-operated</u> switch   _____

7. once in a <u>hundred years</u>   _____

8. make <u>larger</u> with the microscope   _____

9. a change that is <u>by degrees</u>   _____

10. <u>spirited</u> conversation   _____

B. Complete each analogy with a spelling word.

1. **often** is to **frequent** as **yearly** is to   _____

2. **rider** is to **walker** as **passenger** is to   _____

3. **three** is to **triangle** as **four** is to   _____

4. **quiet** is to **active** as **separated** is to   _____

5. **one hundred** is to **twenty-five** as **dollar** is to   _____

6. **two** is to **biped** as **four** is to   _____

7. **far** is to **distant** as **worldwide** is to   _____

8. **ten** is to **decade** as **one hundred** is to   _____

9. **greedy** is to **miserly** as **generous** is to   _____

10. **decrease** is to **reduce** as **increase** is to   _____

Words ending with *ous/us* and *ize/ise*

Teaching

marvel<u>ous</u>	vir<u>us</u>	real<u>ize</u>	desp<u>ise</u>
industri<u>ous</u>	circ<u>us</u>	critic<u>ize</u>	telev<u>ise</u>
adventur<u>ous</u>	cens<u>us</u>	apolog<u>ize</u>	exerc<u>ise</u>
courage<u>ous</u>	geni<u>us</u>	memor<u>ize</u>	advert<u>ise</u>
outrage<u>ous</u>	surpl<u>us</u>	sympath<u>ize</u>	comprom<u>ise</u>

Lesson Generalization: The suffix **ous** is added to words to form adjectives meaning "full of" or "having certain characteristics."

adventurous–full of adventure

The **us** spelling is not a suffix. It is a noun ending.

The suffix **ize** is added to words to form verbs meaning "to make or become."

apologize–to make an apology

The **ise** ending is not a suffix.

A.

1. Adding the suffix **ous** to a word forms an adjective meaning "full of" or "having certain characteristics." Write the words from the word list that are adjectives.

   _____   _____   _____

   _____   _____

2. What ending sounds like the **ous** suffix? _____ What part of speech are words with

   this ending? _____ Write the words from the list with this ending.

   _____   _____   _____

   _____   _____

3. The suffix **ize** can be added to a word to form a verb. Write the **ize** words from the list.

   _____   _____   _____

   _____   _____

4. Like the **ize** suffix, **ise** is often found at the end of a verb. However, **ise** is not a suffix. Write the words from the list that end in **ise**.

   _____   _____   _____

   _____   _____

B. On a seperate sheet of paper, use all of the spelling words in no more than eight sentences. Hint: Combine a noun, a verb, and an adjective in one sentence.

Lesson 27

Words ending with *ous/us* and *ize/ise*

More Practice

1. marvelous	5. outrageous	9. genius	13. apologize	17. televise
2. industrious	6. virus	10. surplus	14. memorize	18. exercise
3. adventurous	7. circus	11. realize	15. sympathize	19. advertise
4. courageous	8. census	12. criticize	16. despise	20. compromise

A. Decide whether **ize** or **ise** should be added to each word or letter group. Write the complete word. Then write the **ing** form of each word.

1. desp _____ _____

2. apology _____ _____

3. comprom _____ _____

4. real _____ _____

5. sympathy _____ _____

6. memory _____ _____

7. telev _____ _____

8. advert _____ _____

9. critic _____ _____

10. exerc _____ _____

B. Use the clues to find spelling words that fit in the puzzle. Hint: You will need to use the past tense of some words.

Across
2. wonderful
4. settled differences
6. hard-working
7. brave
9. say you're sorry
11. to hate
12. daring

Down
1. amount left over
2. committed to memory
3. to know
4. found fault
5. shocking
8. official count
10. brilliant person

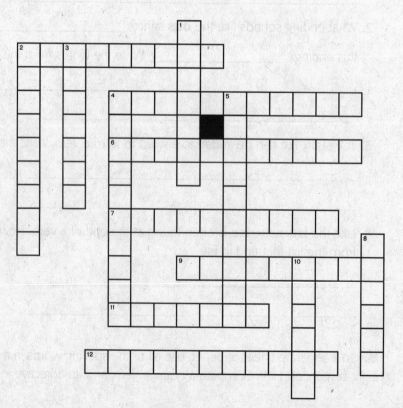

Lesson 28 The prefix *ex*

ex + pect	= expect	ex + tremely	= extremely
ex + pired	= expired	ex + tension	= extension
ex + pert	= expert	ex + tinguish	= extinguish
ex + perience	= experience	ex + terior	= exterior
ex + pensive	= expensive	ex + tinct	= extinct
ex + cuse	= excuse	ex + fort	= effort
ex + clamation	= exclamation	ex + fective	= effective
ex + cursion	= excursion	ex + ficiency	= efficiency
ex + lection	= election	ex + scape	= escape
ex + levate	= elevate	ex + vaporate	= evaporate

Lesson Generalization: When using the prefix **ex,** the letter **x** is never doubled and seldom changes to match the first letter of the root. The challenge in spelling words that begin with the prefix **ex** is caused by the **s** sound of the letter **x**. Do not add the letter **s** between the prefix and the root.

> **ex** remains **ex** before roots that begin with **p, t,** or **c.**
>
> **ex** changes to **ef** when joined to the roots that begin with the letter **f.**
>
> **ex** changes to **e** before most other consonants.

A.

1. The prefix **ex** does not change form before the consonants _____,

_____, and _____. Write the spelling words to which this rule applies.

_____ _____ _____ _____

_____ _____ _____ _____

_____ _____ _____ _____

_____

2. The prefix **ex** changes to _____ before roots that begin with the letter

_____ and to _____ before most other consonants.

Write the spelling words to which this rule applies.

_____ _____ _____ _____

_____ _____

B. On a seperate sheet of paper, write tongue twisters using the words from the spelling list. Use all of the words in as few sentences as possible. Read your twisters to a partner. Try to read your partner's twisters.

Lesson 28 # The prefix *ex*

More Practice

1. expect	6. extremely	11. excuse	16. efficiency
2. expired	7. extension	12. exclamation	17. election
3. expert	8. extinguish	13. excursion	18. elevate
4. experience	9. exterior	14. effort	19. escape
5. expensive	10. extinct	15. effective	20. evaporate

A. A cliché is an expression or idea that has become stale from too much use. "As light as a feather" and "sweet as honey" are clichés. Write the spelling words that could be used in your writing to replace the following clichés.

1. know-it-all _____

2. cost an arm and a leg _____

3. worldly wisdom _____

4. be "on the alert" for _____

5. put out the fire _____

6. dead as a doornail _____

7. flew the coop _____

8. kicked the bucket _____

9. disappear into thin air _____

10. like pulling teeth _____

B. Circle all of the spelling words in the word search puzzle. Then write each word on your own paper.

N	E	E	V	E	Z	W	E	X	T	R	E	M	E	L	Y	E
O	C	X	V	X	E	Q	E	L	E	C	T	I	O	N	E	V
I	N	T	L	T	X	D	E	R	I	P	X	E	Z	V	V	A
T	E	I	O	E	P	R	O	I	R	E	T	X	E	E	I	P
A	I	N	V	N	E	N	O	I	S	R	U	C	X	E	T	O
M	R	C	E	S	N	E	T	A	V	E	L	E	N	J	C	R
A	E	T	X	I	S	I	K	N	T	C	E	P	X	E	E	A
L	P	W	P	O	I	T	E	X	C	U	S	E	R	A	F	T
C	X	X	E	N	V	E	P	A	C	S	E	R	I	D	F	E
X	E	S	R	H	E	Q	S	V	H	C	B	G	K	C	E	W
E	F	D	T	G	H	S	I	U	G	N	I	T	X	E	L	R
Y	C	N	E	I	C	I	F	F	E	E	F	F	O	R	T	T

Lesson 29 Paired prefixes

mis + spelled	= misspelled		ad + resume	= assume
re + spelled	= respelled		re + sume	= resume
dis + solved	= dissolved		sub + ceed	= succeed
re + solved	= resolved		ex + ceed	= exceed
com + mission	= commission		ad + cess	= access
ad + mission	= admission		pro + cess	= process
ad + tend	= attend		com + lapse	= collapse
pre + tend	= pretend		re + lapse	= relapse
ob + fense	= offense		ex + cursion	= excursion
de + fense	= defense		ex + ruption	= eruption

Lesson Generalization: Some double consonants occur because the last letter of the prefix is the same as the first letter of the base word or root: misspelled. Studying the words in each pair will help you to remember that one of the double consonants belongs to the prefix, and one belongs to the root or base word.

Most double consonants occur because the prefix is assimilated. The last letter of the prefix changes to match the first letter of the base word or root:

ad + tend = attend

A.

1. Some double consonants occur when the last letter of the prefix is the same as the first letter of the root. Write three examples from the list.

   _____   _____   _____

2. Other double consonants occur when the last letter of an assimilated prefix changes to match the first letter of the root. Write seven examples from the list.

   _____   _____   _____   _____

   _____   _____   _____

3. Perhaps the easiest words to spell are those that join the prefix to the root word without any spelling changes in either part. Write those words from the list.

   _____   _____   _____   _____

   _____   _____   _____   _____

   _____   _____

B. On a separate sheet of paper, write ten original sentences. Use a different pair of words from the spelling list in each sentence. Use all the words.

Paired prefixes

More Practice

1. misspelled	5. commission	9. offense	13. succeed	17. collapse
2. respelled	6. admission	10. defense	14. exceed	18. relapse
3. dissolved	7. attend	11. assume	15. access	19. corruption
4. resolved	8. pretend	12. resume	16. process	20. eruption

A. Complete each sentence with two spelling words that contain the same root.

1. Only two scientists have _____ to the secret _____.

2. The football coach praised both the _____ and the _____.

3. Will this year's fund-raising drive _____ in its attempt to _____ its goal.

4. The student _____ each word that she had _____ on the pretest.

5. The newspaper's accusations of _____ resulted in an _____ of angry denials from several officials.

6. Mark tried to _____ that he was thrilled to _____ the boring meeting.

7. I _____ that the show will _____ after the special news report.

8. As the decorations _____ in the rain, Sue _____ never to have an outdoor party again.

9. The college established a _____ to study its _____ policies.

10. A _____ of his illness caused the patient to _____ in exhaustion.

B. Use the clues below to help you complete the crossword puzzle with words from the spelling list.

Across

1. a share or part

3. spelled again

4. evil

7. liquefied

9. outburst

10. to go beyond the expected

11. to happen again

Down

2. spelled incorrectly

5. decided

6. counterattack

8. entrance

Lesson 30 **Words from the French language**   *Teaching*

amateur	tongue	bureau	corsage	beret
chauffeur	league	plateau	mirage	ballet
grandeur	fatigue	trousseau	espionage	buffet
pasteurize	vague	chateau	sabotage	gourmet

Lesson Generalization: Spelling follows certain patterns in every language. Some French letter patterns appear in words commonly used in the English language: **eur**, **eau**, final silent **t**, final silent **ue**.

In both English and French, a soft **g** is usually followed by **e, i**, or **y**. The hard **g** is usually followed by **a**, **o**, or **u**.

A.

1. Not only do some French spelling patterns appear in English, but so too does the pronunciation of those letter combinations. Find and write words from the word list that have the following French letter patterns and pronunciation:

eur	eau	final silent t	final silent ue
_____	_____	_____	_____
_____	_____	_____	_____
_____	_____	_____	_____
_____	_____	_____	_____

2. In both English and French, a soft **g** is usually followed by _____,

_____, or _____. What words from the list have a soft **g**?

_____ _____ _____ _____

The hard **g** usually precedes _____, _____, or

_____. What words from the list have a hard **g** near the end of the word?

_____ _____ _____ _____

B. On a seperate sheet of paper, write a short story using as many words as possible from the spelling list—12 or more. Share your story with a partner or small group.

Lesson 30

Words from the French language

More Practice

1. amateur	5. bureau	9. beret	13. tongue	17. corsage
2. chauffeur	6. plateau	10. ballet	14. league	18. mirage
3. grandeur	7. trousseau	11. buffet	15. fatigue	19. espionage
4. pasteurize	8. chateau	12. gourmet	16. vague	20. sabotage

A. Complete each sentence with a spelling word.

1. Does the dairy farm _____ its own milk?

2. Jeffrey reads books about spies because he likes tales of _____.

3. A high, flat stretch of land is called a _____.

4. The initials F.B.I. stand for the Federal _____ of Investigation.

5. The agents planned to _____ the railroads of the enemy's country.

6. Only _____ players can enter this special tournament.

7. The _____ image of a lake in the desert was only a _____.

8. Tourists are always impressed by the _____ of the French Alps.

9. The _____ driving that limousine is wearing a _____.

10. Doctors say that the exhausted athlete is suffering from _____.

B. Unscramble these spelling words and write them on the lines. Hint: The French letter patterns are not scrambled.

1. euraamt _____

2. eterb _____

3. ontueg _____

4. etmougr _____

5. eaurtsous _____

6. hctaeau _____

7. imrage _____

8. scroage _____

9. ffbuet _____

10. etllba _____

11. tobsaage _____

12. uaffeurhc _____

13. eziptsaeur _____

14. pteaual _____

15. rbueau _____

16. eurngrad _____

17. uegtifa _____

18. gvaue _____

19. agenoispe _____

20. aleueg _____

Lesson 31 Silent *gh*

<u>ough</u>t	d<u>ough</u>nut	sl<u>igh</u>t	h<u>eigh</u>t
alth<u>ough</u>	f<u>ough</u>t	del<u>igh</u>tful	w<u>eigh</u>ed
thr<u>ough</u>out	br<u>ough</u>t	s<u>igh</u>tseeing	<u>eigh</u>tieth
thor<u>ough</u>ly	b<u>ough</u>t	fr<u>igh</u>tened	fr<u>eigh</u>t
thor<u>ough</u>bred	th<u>ough</u>tless	copyr<u>igh</u>t	n<u>eigh</u>borhood

Lesson Generalization: The letters **gh** are silent in a few familiar letter combinations:

ou**gh**   i**gh**t   ei**gh**

A.

1. Write the spelling words that have the familiar letter combination **ough**.

_____   _____   _____

_____   _____   _____

_____   _____   _____

_____

2. What spelling words have the **ight** letter combination?

_____   _____   _____

_____   _____

3. In which spelling words can you find the **eigh** pattern?

_____   _____   _____

_____   _____

B. Correctly write the misspelled words below.

1. siteseeying _____
2. buyght _____
3. threwout _____
4. throughly _____
5. faught _____
6. frayt _____
7. hight _____
8. nayborhood _____
9. alltho _____
10. dilitefull _____

Lesson 31 **Silent _gh_**

1. ought	6. doughnut	11. slight	16. height
2. although	7. fought	12. delightful	17. weighed
3. throughout	8. brought	13. sightseeing	18. eightieth
4. thoroughly	9. bought	14. frightened	19. freight
5. thoroughbred	10. thoughtless	15. copyright	20. neighborhood

A. Write the spelling words that contain the following words:

ought

_____

_____

_____

_____

_____

rough

_____

_____

_____

eight

_____

_____

_____

light

_____

_____

right

_____

_____

B. Complete these analogies. The first two words will be either synonyms or antonyms. Write the spelling word that will make the same relationship between the next two words.

1. **generous** is to **stingy** as **considerate** is to _____

2. **may** is to **might** as **should** is to _____

3. **up** is to **down** as **width** is to _____

4. **big** is to **large** as **slender** is to _____

5. **hot** is to **cold** as **unpleasant** is to _____

6. **restaurant** is to **eating** as **vacation** is to _____

7. **ship** is to **boat** as **cargo** is to _____

8. **illegally** is to **lawfully** as **incompletely** is to _____

9. **under** is to **below** as **during** is to _____

10. **maybe** is to **perhaps** as **though** is to _____

11. **finished** is to **concluded** as **counted** is to _____

Lesson 32 | Review

1. stereotype	9. courageous	17. experience	25. bureau
2. stereophonic	10. virus	18. extremely	26. league
3. archeology	11. memorize	19. misspelled	27. thoroughly
4. technology	12. realize	20. dissolved	28. weighted
5. unanimous	13. exercise	21. process	29. frightened
6. centigrade	14. excuse	22. succeed	30. neighborhood
7. anniversary	15. effort	23. amateur	
8. manufacture	16. escape	24. chauffeur	

A. Complete each analogy with a word from the spelling list.

1. **circuses** is to **circus** as **viruses** is to _____

2. **complete** is to **completely** as **extreme** is to _____

3. **proved** is to **disproved** as **solved** is to _____

4. **critic** is to **criticize** as **real** is to _____

5. **industriously** is to **industrious** as **unanimously** is to _____

6. **outrage** is to **outrageous** as **courage** is to _____

7. **rough** is to **roughly** as **thorough** is to _____

8. **exploding** is to **explode** as **escaping** is to _____

9. **matched** is to **mismatched** as **spelled** is to _____

10. **apology** is to **apologize** as **memory** is to _____

11. **tongues** is to **tongue** as **leagues** is to _____

12. **fatigued** is to **fatigue** as **chauffeured** is to _____

13. **unexplored** is to **explore** as **unexcused** is to _____

14. **beginners** is to **beginner** as **amateurs** is to _____

15. **excess** is to **exceed** as **success** is to _____

B. On a seperate sheet of paper, create a word search puzzle using at least 20 words from the spelling list. Trade papers with a partner and solve each other's puzzles.

Lesson 32 # Review

A. Three of the words in each row follow the same spelling pattern. Write the word that does not follow the same pattern.

1. architect   patriarch   psychic   stereophonic   _____
2. marvelous   surplus   census   genius   _____
3. expect   expensive   extension   effective   _____
4. vague   corsage   fatigue   tongue   _____
5. apologize   criticize   despise   sympathize   _____
6. exclamation   elevate   election   evaporate   _____
7. manuscript   centigrade   quadruped   magnify   _____
8. access   process   attend   assume   _____
9. beret   ballet   weighed   gourmet   _____
10. genesis   centipede   hydrant   phobia   _____

B. Complete each analogy with a word from the list. Each word is used once.

| pedestrian | quadruped | chateau | expense | beret | ballet |
| paternal | tongue | genesis | exterior | amateur | vague |

1. **fruit** is to **apple** as **hat** is to   _____
2. **man** is to **dog** as **biped** is to   _____
3. **food** is to **doughnut** as **dance** is to   _____
4. **car** is to **limousine** as **house** is to   _____
5. **touch** is to **finger** as **taste** is to   _____
6. **hate** is to **despise** as **cost** is to   _____
7. **busy** is to **industrious** as **origin** is to   _____
8. **mother** is to **father** as **maternal** is to   _____
9. **vehicle** is to **driver** as **foot** is to   _____
10. **internal** is to **external** as **interior** is to _____
11. **expert** is to **professional** as **novice** is to _____
12. **lively** is to **animated** as **unclear** is to   _____